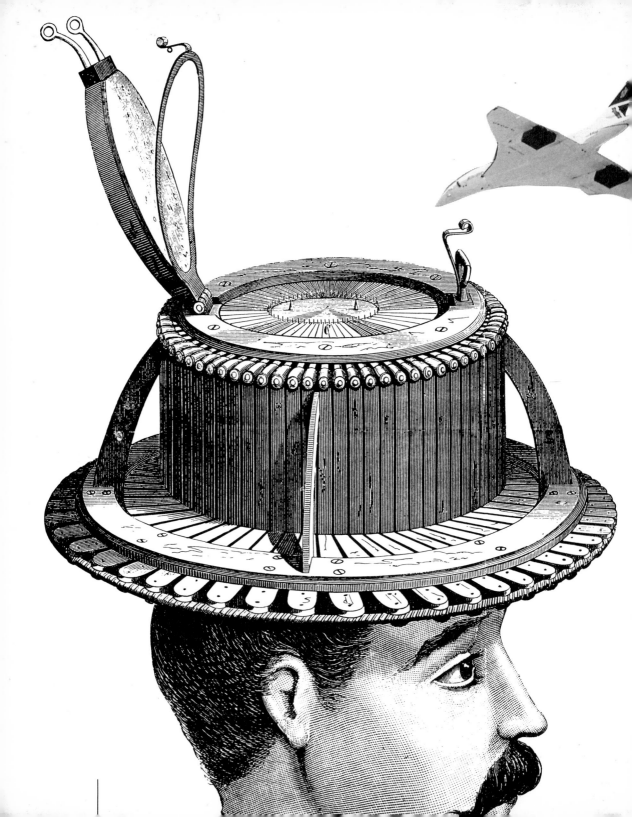

Measure
for Measure

Fascinating facts about Length, Weight, Time and Temperature

SALLY DUGAN

BBC BOOKS

WINDFALL FILMS

This book is published to accompany the television series entitled *Measure for Measure* which was first broadcast in 1993
Published by BBC Books,
a division of BBC Enterprises Limited,
Woodlands, 80 Wood Lane
London W12 0TT

First Published 1993
© Windfall Films 1993
ISBN 0 563 36900 0

Designed by Hammond Hammond
Illustrations by Russell Jones, Simon Roulstone, Roger Hammond
Set in Century ITC by Goodfellow & Egan Ltd, Cambridge
Printed and bound in Great Britain by Butler & Tanner Ltd, Frome and London.
Cover printed by Clays Ltd, St Ives plc

CONTENTS

PREFACE

EVER SINCE CAVE people decided that one boulder-weight of mammoth steak was worth two large nose bones, measurement has been an essential part of everyday life. The desire to measure is almost as old as a sense of fairness.

Yet few people give more than a passing thought to the origins of the measures we use today. This book – like the four-part BBC series it is designed to accompany – aims to romp rather than plod through the history of measurement. It may not be as accurate, say, as the atomic clock which ticks over nine billion times a second, but it should make you want to find out more and, for that reason, a bibliography is included at the end of the book.

Measure for Measure would not have been possible without the ideas and loony enthusiasm of Ian Duncan, who produced the series, aided and abetted by Bryn Higgins. My thanks go to the Windfall Films production team: Lucy Hannah, Annabel Lee, Robert Davis, and to Windfall's Company Manager, Anne Cafferky. Seton Bennett, Chief Executive of the Weights and Measures Laboratory, and Jonathan Betts of the National Maritime Museum very kindly checked the manuscript, but should bear no responsibility for any mistakes which may have crept in. Special thanks also go to my husband David Dugan, and to my children Christopher and Emily, who asked the questions no one else thought to ask.

LENGTH

'Man is the measure of all things'

(PROTAGORAS, C.490–421 BC)

ONE OF THE biggest draws at the Trocadero in Piccadilly Circus, London, is Robert Wadlow, the tallest man in the history of the world. Visitors flock to rub their noses on his waistcoat buttons, stomp in his footsteps and match their hands against his – all in replica.

People have always used their bodies as yardsticks – sometimes quite literally. The Egyptians measured with digits, palms and cubits. (A cubit is the distance from the elbow to the tip of the middle finger.) The Greeks and Romans and countless others since have used feet but, since no two bodies are the same, it is a pretty vague method of measurement, which is why people introduced standards. The Egyptians used a black granite master stick – Charlemagne used his own foot.

STANDARDS In a battle, an army fixes up a standard as a rallying point for the troops. If that standard were to move, confusion would reign. So, in measurement, the word 'standard' has come to mean a fixed length, weight or volume. In Britain, the idea of using lengths or lumps of metal as standards has been around since Anglo-Saxon times.

Born in February 1918 in Illinois, in the US, Robert Wadlow weighed $8^1/2$ lb (3.8 kg) at birth, but started his astonishing spurt of growth from the age of two. At five, he was 5 foot 4 inches (1.6 metres) tall, at 10 he was 6 foot 5 inches (1.9 metres). By the time he died, at the age of 22, he was 8 foot 11 inches (2.7 metres) and still growing. His death came as a result of a septic blister on his ankle, caused by a poorly fitting brace. Had he lived today, he would never have grown that tall. His problem was probably a malfunction of the pituitary gland, now easily curable.

THE
TALLEST
MAN

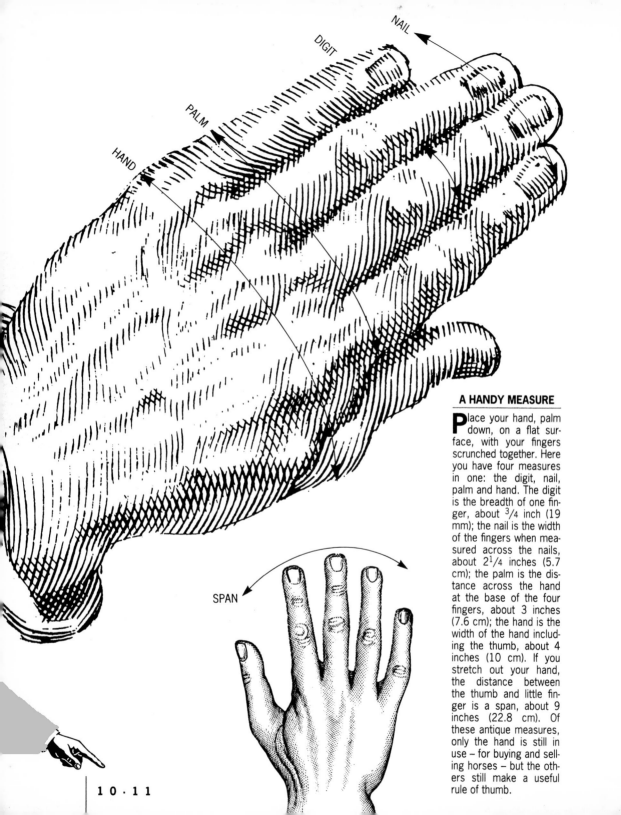

NAIL

DIGIT

PALM

HAND

SPAN

A HANDY MEASURE

Place your hand, palm down, on a flat surface, with your fingers scrunched together. Here you have four measures in one: the digit, nail, palm and hand. The digit is the breadth of one finger, about $3/4$ inch (19 mm); the nail is the width of the fingers when measured across the nails, about $2^1/4$ inches (5.7 cm); the palm is the distance across the hand at the base of the four fingers, about 3 inches (7.6 cm); the hand is the width of the hand including the thumb, about 4 inches (10 cm). If you stretch out your hand, the distance between the thumb and little finger is a span, about 9 inches (22.8 cm). Of these antique measures, only the hand is still in use – for buying and selling horses – but the others still make a useful rule of thumb.

THE ULTIMATE METAL BAR Early metal yardsticks – which were copied and used all over the country – were based on the length of the sovereign's arm (hence the name 'imperial' measurements). It was better than nothing, but still rather arbitrary. One snag with these early standards was that the ends got knocked and worn away, rendering them virtually useless. So, by the seventeenth century, the idea of using lines or brass pins to mark the length had become popular.

The real breakthrough, however, came in 1834, when the set of imperial standards went up in flames with the Houses of Parliament. At the time, it must have seemed like an unmitigated disaster. In fact, it was a blessing in disguise.

The imperial pound disappeared among the ashes, never to be found again. The imperial yard – the standard since 1760 – survived, but it was in such a pitiful state that it might as well have been consumed by the flames. Even before the fire, the dots that were supposed to define its length had been badly cratered by compass points. When the heat of the flames melted one of the golden plugs surrounding these craters, the standard became completely useless.

STARTING FROM SCRATCH It may seem unlikely, but the original plan was to make a new yard bar using something we normally associate with clocks – a pendulum.

Way back in the sixteenth century, Galileo had found that the time of a pendulum swing varied according to its length. Complicated scientific calculations since then had established what length of pendulum would be needed to count the seconds in different places. (Gravity is stronger in

Fire broke out at the old Houses of Parliament on 16 October 1834. A pile of wooden Exchequer tallies – which were used when coins were in short supply – were being burnt, and the fire got out of hand. All that remained of the original royal Palace of Westminster was the medieval Great Hall, the chapel with its crypt and cloisters, and the Jewel Tower. But the fire, which seemed so devastating at the time, had its advantages. It gave us Big Ben, and the imposing Gothic Houses of Parliament which are now so familiar. It also gave scientists a unique opportunity to rethink the way they looked at standards of measurement.

some parts of the world than others, and the strength or weakness of the G-force affects the speed of a pendulum's swing.)

An Act of Parliament had decreed that if anything happened to the imperial yard, it could be restored using Galileo's principle. All you had to do was to set up a pendulum to beat seconds at a known latitude, and you could calculate its length. At least that was the theory. But scientists soon found this was easier said than done. Despite the law, they abandoned the idea.

Instead, they decided to call in all the other standards they could find and see how they compared with each other. First, though, they had to construct suitable apparatus. It was a task that was to take twelve years, and see two men into their graves.

Scientific myth has it that Galileo first discovered the principle of the pendulum by watching the swings of a large candelabra at Pisa Cathedral. Later scientists worked out that a pendulum beating seconds at the latitude of London would be 39.1399 inches (99.4153 cm) long. The idea was to reconstruct the yard using this formula, but making the pendulum, and suitably accurate measuring apparatus, proved too difficult.

MEASURING THE MEASURING STICKS Two unpaid enthusiasts supervised the work: Francis Baily, and the Rev. Richard Sheepshanks. Both were men with large private incomes and seemingly insatiable appetites for experiment.

Baily concentrated on finding the right metal for a new bar, dropping various combinations of brass and gun-metal from great heights and loading them up with weights. Eventually he came up with a mixture that was 16 parts copper, 2.5 parts tin and 1 part zinc. This was used when the new standard finally came to be made, and the name given to the material – Baily's metal – is his memorial.

After Baily died in August 1844, his mantle passed to the Rev. Sheepshanks. He travelled tirelessly from his home in Reading up to London, even though his own health was failing, too.

The new bar was born in the dark and gloomy cellars of Somerset House – then the headquarters of the Royal Astronomical Society. Great hunks of masonry were carted down to the cellars to make vibration-free foundations for the apparatus. Micrometer microscopes and troughs of mercury – in which to float the bars – were all in place. It was then that the process hit a snag. In a warm room, a metal bar will expand and so be slightly longer than in a cold room. But where were the thermometers sensitive enough to measure the tiny variations in temperature that could make such a difference? Work ground to a halt while a suitably accurate thermometer was made.

Another snag came when scientists realised that heat from the lights they worked under could affect the results for the same reason. Once again, everyone downed tools until a more sophisticated lighting system could be devised.

When the work of comparison eventually began, it was exhaustive. More than 200,000

Francis Baily (1774–1844) was an adventurer, businessman and amateur astronomer. Having made his fortune in the City, he had the luxury of being able to retire at the early age of 51 to concentrate on what really interested him. He set up house in Tavistock Place in London and spent many happy hours there glued to his telescope, or setting up indescribably complicated scientific experiments. Even before the standard yard was destroyed, he had been working on pendulums and length. So when a Royal Commission was appointed in 1838 to look into ways of producing a new standard, he was an obvious candidate to choose.

The Rev. Richard Sheepshanks (1794–1855) was qualified as a barrister and clergyman, but never worked as either. His early public work was in setting electoral district boundaries between the Thames and the Humber, but science and astronomy were his first loves. He was a lifelong Fellow of Trinity College, Cambridge, and is commemorated in a plaque in the College Chapel, opposite a statue of Sir Isaac Newton.

readings were taken, with identical experiments repeated several times so as to rule out any possibility of human error. Eventually a total of 40 new standard bars were made, with the best chosen as the main standards. The Number One standard was deposited at Westminster, 'In the custody of the Right Honourable the Comptroller of the Exchequer'. Others were placed at the Royal Mint, the Royal Society, the Royal Observatory in Greenwich and at imperial outposts all over the globe.

Exhausted by his labours on the yard's behalf, the Rev. Sheepshanks died of a stroke on 29 July 1855. The Act legalising the new standard received the Royal Assent just the day after his death.

THE FATE OF THE YARD Mindful of the fate of the original yard standard, a copy was carefully bricked up into a fire-proof cavity in a wall of the newly built House of Commons. Resting on eight rollers inside a mahogany box, it had the further protection of a leaden outer casket which in turn was enclosed in oak. Every 20 years, the wall was unbricked and the casket cut open in the presence of the Lord Chancellor, the Lord Chamberlain, the Speaker and the President of the Board of Trade. The standard was checked, and then cemented inside the wall again.

Despite the labour that went into making it, the imperial standard was soon overtaken by events. The United States abandoned their copy of the imperial yard only 11 years after it

The imperial standard yard is a 38 inch (96.5 cm) long metal bar, with two holes an inch in from either end, each containing a gold plug. The bar is marked 'Copper 16 oz Tin 2 $\frac{1}{2}$ Zinc 1. Mr Baily's Metal. No. 1 STANDARD YARD at 62 .00 Faht. Cast in 1845 Troughton & Simms, LONDON.' Copies were distributed all over the Empire, with careful notes of the exact temperature at which they measured a yard. Copy Number 7 went to the East India Company, and Number 17 to the colony of the Cape of Good Hope.

became legal, deciding instead to link their yard to the French metre. This may have been

partly political but it also turned out to be practical. Tests have shown that the British standard has been steadily shrinking by one part in a million every 23 years. You might reasonably ask, who cares? But engineers and scientists do.

During the Second World War, the difference between the English and the American inch caused problems when the two countries tried to swop aircraft parts. An ill-fitting aircraft part is not simply a matter of taste, like an ill-fitting suit. It is a matter of life and death. These differences were ironed out in the 1950s, when an international value for the English and American yard was set between the two. Both

Bronze plaques showing standards of length were exhibited in public places so traders and workmen could check their own measures. One such plaque was installed in the vestibule of the Science Galleries at the South Kensington Museum in 1893 'so that any workman can at once test his two-foot rule to one hundredth of an inch'. It now rests in the Science Museum in London. Other London plaques can be seen on the north wall of Trafalgar Square and outside the Royal Observatory at Greenwich.

This 30 metre laser interferometer is surely a candidate for the ultimate ruler, with its shiny metal tubing and flickering red digital read-out. More than a century separates it from Baily's metal bar, but both are trying to do the same job. Standards of length are now set by the speed of light, using machines like this one at the National Weights and Measures Laboratory in Teddington, Middlesex. The metre is defined as the distance travelled by light in just under one three hundred millionth of a second, and the yard is defined by its relationship to the metre.

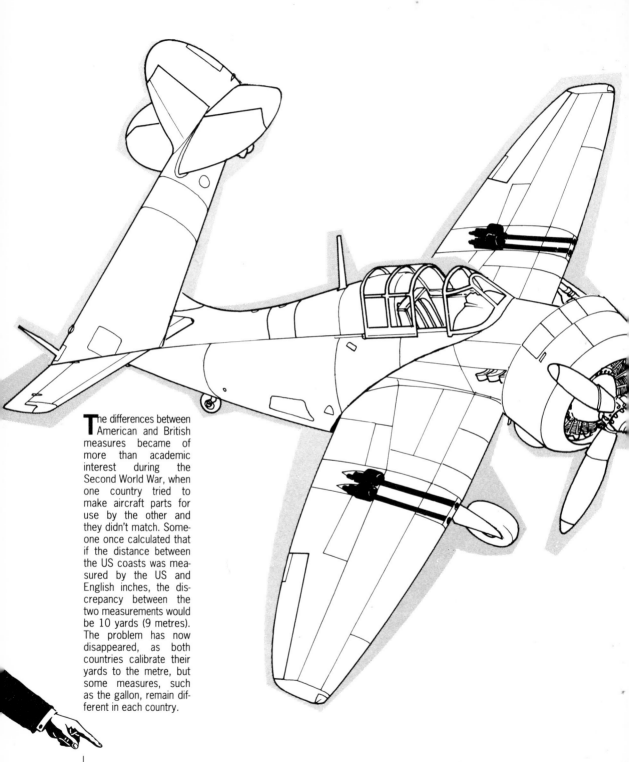

The differences between American and British measures became of more than academic interest during the Second World War, when one country tried to make aircraft parts for use by the other and they didn't match. Someone once calculated that if the distance between the US coasts was measured by the US and English inches, the discrepancy between the two measurements would be 10 yards (9 metres). The problem has now disappeared, as both countries calibrate their yards to the metre, but some measures, such as the gallon, remain different in each country.

yards are now calibrated to the metre, and yardsticks survive only as historical curiosities.

METRICATION RULES!   Since 1963, when an Act of Parliament redefined British weights and measures in terms of the metric system, metrication has been a fact of life. By the end of 1999, the yard will have been consigned to history.

Not all the old measures have been eased out so painlessly. The mile and the pint, apparently as symbolic of British sovereignty as the Crown Jewels, are to stay. Government ministers clearly know when they are on to a vote-loser. 'We're not going to have to re-measure the cricket pitch', an Orwellian-sounding Corporate Affairs Minister reassured readers of *The Times* in 1988. And, in 1991, the *Evening Standard* reported that John Major was 'the toast of the nation… after saving the Great British Pinta from Brussels.'

Nationalism rears its ugly head more than once in the story of measurement, as we shall see in the tale of the metre.

THE MEN WHO MEASURED THE EARTH   A   new,   rational scheme of measurement based on nature, instead of the irregular human body, was part of the brave new world promised by the French Revolution of the eighteenth century.

The word metre, taken from the Greek, *metron*, means 'measure', and the French idea was to make it the basis of a system that operated in multiples of ten. But first, they had to decide how long the metre was to be.

Nothing was too much trouble for scientists in the eighteenth century – they thought global, but even they accepted that measuring the entire earth was rather impractical. So they settled for something a little more modest. The metre, it was decided, should be one ten-millionth of the distance between the North Pole and the Equator. But how far was that?

In 1792, two engineers – Jean Delambre and Pierre Méchain – set out to measure the distance between Dunkirk and Barcelona. These two places were chosen because both were in apparently friendly territory, both at sea level and both on the same meridian, or line of longitude. The plan was to take the measurements with military precision and then use them to calculate the larger distance.

They did not, of course, measure every step of the way. Rather, they used the principle of triangulation: if you know one side and two angles, or two sides and one angle, of any triangle you can calculate its other parts. So, with their surveying instruments, Delambre and Méchain constructed a string of connected imaginary triangles all the way from Dunkirk to Barcelona.

But it was not as easy as it might sound. Firstly, the base lines of their triangles – each between 1 and 10 kilometres ($\frac{1}{2}$ and 6 miles) long – had to be staked out with rods, bars or steel tapes, carefully laid end to end. Correction had to be made for temperature and the curvature of the earth and, for measuring stations above sea level, allowance also had to be made for height.

As if this wasn't enough, they had to make endless astronomical observations to pinpoint latitude. Each man made 1800 observations of the Pole Star, for example, to discover the exact position of the Pantheon in Paris, which formed one of the points of their triangles.

SPIES! All these practical problems paled, however, beside the political ones. From the outset, the enterprise was inextricably linked with the turmoil of the times. On 19 June 1791 a committee of 12 scientists had met with Louis XVI to get his formal approval for the surveys to take place. But the very next day the King was put under arrest for attempting to escape from France. It wasn't until a year later that he issued the proclamation from his cell enabling Delambre and Méchain to get to work.

They divided up the work between them, with Delambre taking the northern part of the meridian and Méchain the southern. Delambre's chunk of the work was three times the size of his partner's, but this was mainly because his was the easier territory and also because it had been measured twice before. Armed only with the King's proclamation and the tools of their trade, the pair set off. However, their triangulation beacons and white survey flags soon attracted attention of the most unwelcome kind. White was, after all, the royal colour – and why light beacons, unless you are a spy signalling to other spies?

Daily or weekly interrogations by committees on Un-French Activities soon became their lot, and they wasted many hours kicking their heels in provincial lock-ups. It took seven years for Delambre and Méchain to complete their survey, by which time many of the original team back in Paris had been imprisoned or guillotined.

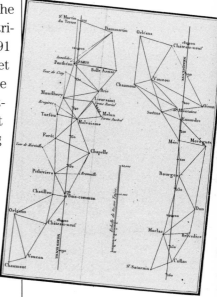

Illustrations in Méchain and Delambre's account of their measurements for the metre look like futuristic architectural drawings, because of their complicated interconnected triangles.

FOR ALL PEOPLE? The metric system finally became a fact in June 1799, and the motto adopted for the new system was 'For all people, for all time'. It was a great slogan, but unfortunately rather wide of the truth.

In France itself, metrication did not exactly sweep all before it. People in backward rural areas simply carried on as before, in a highly effective form of passive resistance. Napoleon, who was by then Emperor, was forced into issuing a decree allowing people to use the old measures after all, and it was not until 1840 that the metre and all its fellow measurements were established as the legal monopoly.

In some countries, metric measures have been adopted during the course of political upheaval, just as in their French beginnings. Latin America, the former Soviet Union and China are all notable examples.

THE GREAT MISSED CHANCE Way back in 1790, when the French statesman Talleyrand first canvassed the marvels of metrication, he had hoped to secure the co-operation of both Britain and the United States. However, although other European countries tagged along, both Britain and the United States stayed aloof. Looking at the measuring muddle that followed, this must rate as one of the greatest missed chances in scientific history.

The main reason for the rejection of metric measurements was political. Britain was reluctant to be seen to support what it saw as a highly questionable regime, and the United States was reluctant to rock the diplomatic boat with its newly-vanquished foe.

President George Washington, who had started out life as a land surveyor, was well aware of the need for a rational system of measurement. He tackled the subject in 1790, in the first-ever presidential address to Congress. A select committee was appointed to look into the problem but, as happens all too often with committees, it floundered in its own verbiage.

Thomas Jefferson had at one stage advocated a decimal system based on the seconds pendulum but, for nationalistic reasons, would not countenance one based on a line in France. How would the Americans ever be able to verify it? Because nothing was done about it, and people still used the old imperial measurements, the idea of changing to metric became more and more of an ordeal.

In this century, a voluntary metrication programme was introduced into the United States, but it was not notably successful. In fact, twenty-five million dollars were cut from the price of the MX missile system simply by cancelling the requirement that every part of it should be metric.

Old habits die hard.

THE LENGTHS PEOPLE GO TO... Watch someone as they stand in front of a mirror and you will see them visibly smarten up. Shoulders back, stomach in – it's a natural human instinct. However, it's not a very helpful one if you are trying to measure someone for a suit. Tailors need to know about the dropped shoulders and fatal flab, otherwise their customers might as well buy their clothes at the nearest chain store.

The problem of taking accurate measurements has exercised tailors for centuries. *Le Tailleur Sincère*, published in Paris in 1671, is the earliest known French work on tailoring. Its author, M. Boullay, advises 'Observe well a man before measuring him, so as to note his ordinary posture, and that without warning him, for he may stoop naturally or hold himself erect, or else lean on one side or the other; if he expects that you are going to take his measure, he will think he is doing right to hold himself more erect than usual and you will fail with your measure.'

At Gieves and Hawkes, the royal tailors in Savile Row, London, the cutters often deal with two or three generations of the same family. They make notes on their paper patterns to remind them of which topics will put their customers at ease and which will make them stand to attention. The last thing they want is to mention a taboo subject which will put a customer on his guard.

'The cutter has to build up a relationship of trust. He has to be not only a craftsman, but a diplomat,' said Robert Gieve, who is himself a walking advertisement for his firm, in a trim navy double-breasted suit with a yellow silk handkerchief.

Gieves and Hawkes specialises in the bespoke suit, which is a cut above made-to-measure, with a price tag to match (at the time of writing, it is thirteen hundred pounds or more, depending on the material).

'A lot of people think made-to-measure is the ultimate, but it's not,' said Mr Gieve. 'It's individual in the sense that it's taken proper regard of your size and measures, but it's by no means uniquely created for you. You never meet the craftspeople who are going to cut it for you or sew it. That's done somewhere else, where they receive the measures, then adapt a suit to fit the measure.'

The customer of the bespoke suit chooses the cloth and the style, together with any extras he may want (such as deeper pockets, wider lapels or extra buttons). Then comes the ritual of measuring. The cutter takes the measurements of every possible segment of the body and calls them out to the salesman. Not only numbers, but letters, too – the cutter's code for a less-than-standard body.

The uniform which Admiral Lord Nelson was wearing when he was fatally wounded at the Battle of Trafalgar can be seen – complete with bullet hole – at the Maritime Museum in Greenwich. Supplied by Gieves and Hawkes, its size is a reminder of how much taller people have become. Visitors who go round HMS *Victory*, Nelson's flagship, at Portsmouth have to stoop, but its original occupants would have fitted it perfectly.

'If a man's with his wife or a girlfriend, you can't call out "full stomach, flat-footed, bow-legged". So you call out letters – FS for full stomach, and so on.'

The complete ritual is not strictly necessary for an existing customer, because the company will already have a paper cut-out of his shape. Even so, the cutter will have to check that the customer has not lost or gained weight and, in any case, according to Mr Gieve, people sometimes feel cheated if they don't get the full treatment. He has been known to call out a list of well-known initials, such as BA or AA, just to keep the customer happy. 'It's quite difficult to keep a straight face – it's pure mischief, to let them feel they're getting the works.'

The measures are written on to garment tickets, then taken up into the attic cutting room. Here, with the aid of giant Struwwelpeter-like scissors, the paper patterns are created and the suit takes form. Tricks of the trade – like the 'stomach cut', which is an extra dart to accommodate a pot belly – can streamline a figure highly effectively, but a tailor can't disguise something if he doesn't know it's there. Once the suit is tacked together, it will be tried on, then pulled apart again for a final sewing.

Bespoke suits are obviously popular with those who have less-than-standard figures, but Gieves and Hawkes also do a large trade in military uniforms. Up in the tailors' workroom, red mess jackets with shiny gold braid and lovat green tunics hang beside the pin-striped city suits.

Military and dress uniforms were the original reason for the company's existence. Founded in 1785, Gieves and Hawkes numbered the Duke of Wellington, Admiral Lord Nelson and his Flag Captain Hardy among their early customers. It is, in fact, on record that Hardy took lodgings

A red velvet-lined display case, used in the Great Exhibition of 1851, shows the range of uniforms produced by Gieves and Hawkes at the time. Uniformity of measurement, as well as of colour and material, is essential.

above the shop itself in 1827.

During the Crimean War in the 1850s, Gieves and Hawkes fitted and sent out a yacht to operate as a tailors' workshop. They were also one of the earliest companies to offer mail-order. Pride of place in the company's Savile Row shop is given to a gentleman's detachable shirt collar which was sent through the post in 1908, with an order on the back for two dozen more of the same. The address was given simply as HMS Hawke – Manoeuvring.

If careful measurement is essential in tailoring, it is doubly so in uniforms. 'Accuracy is vital – you have to measure not only to fit the wearer, but to ensure uniformity,' said Mr Gieve. The gold lace curl on a naval cuff, for instance, has to be exactly $9/16$ inch (14 mm) wide, no more and no less.

FINGERPRINTING THE HEAD The average head size is $7^1/4$, hat sizes like shoe sizes being made up of apparently arbitrary numbers. If you measure the circumference of your head in inches, and divide it by three, that should give you your rough hat size.

At Gieves and Hawkes, they have a gruesome-looking machine, called a conformature, which has been measuring heads since 1886. It is still in use for hard hats – squashy hats do not need such exact measurement.

According to Mr Gieve, headprints could be used for identification in the same way as fingerprints. 'We all have heads of totally different sizes – and not only sizes, but configurations,' said Mr Gieve. 'It's nothing to do with being a man or a woman. It's just whether we fell out of the pram, or

This may look like an archaic instrument of torture, but it is actually a device for measuring heads. The conformature measures the circumference of the head at the point where a hat headband would rest. Steel spikes at the top of the device punch holes into a paper pattern, which gives a miniature blueprint of the head.

whether we were subjected to strange pressures in the mother's womb… who knows? We're all different.'

FROM THE CRADLE TO THE GRAVE There's a tape-measure for everything, from babies (British mothers like to know their children's length in inches, not centimetres) to corpses.

Undertakers have a special 7-foot (2.1 metre) measure, and in the old days they used to take the coffin to the house to try it for size. As one undertaker put it: 'A coffin fits you better than an off-the-peg suit.' The crucial measurements are the width across the shoulders and hips and, of course, the length. Coffins used to be made individually but now they come ready-made and vary from 5 feet 3 inches (1.6 metres) to 6 feet 6 inches (1.9 metres) in length. Rectangular caskets are more expensive than the traditional coffin-shaped ones.

When hanging was still in force as a means of capital punishment, the Home Office provided a table showing the length of drop necessary for instant death, according to the weight of the prisoner. If the rope was too long, it would rip the head clean off. If too short, it would not give the clean neck-break needed. Albert Pierrepoint, Britain's most famous hangman, found the age and strength of the prisoner also made a difference and would make secret trials with sandbags the night before an execution.

Britain's most famous hangman, who died in July 1992 at the age of 87, took a pride in his work. Knowing that measurement was crucial, Albert Pierrepoint made careful calculations to achieve the swiftest possible results during an execution. One hanging at Strangeways Prison took a mere $7^1/2$ seconds. Among the 433 men and 17 women he hanged during his career were Nazi war criminals, including 9 responsible for atrocities in Belsen. He also officiated at the executions of John Christie, Timothy Evans (who was posthumously pardoned) and Ruth Ellis.

OF NIPPLE-WARMERS AND OTHER HIDDEN CHALLENGES

More than six out of every ten women are walking around in the wrong size bra, according to June Kenton from the London corsetry firm, Rigby and Peller. Most wear what she delicately describes as 'nipple-warmers', because the sizing is so confusing.

The problem is that women think they know what size they are but, because manufacturers' sizes differ so much, there is no such thing as the 'right' size for them. Big chain stores will buy bras from as many as a dozen different manufacturers, then apply their own sizing to them, which only adds to the confusion.

On an even more intimate level, there is the question of the condom. The British standard is 160 mm which is approximately $6^1/2$ inches long, but the European standard is 170 mm (nearly 7 inches long). What does this say about European men?

SIZING UP SHOES Shoe sizes are a law unto themselves. Imperial sizes start at size 0 for children – a measurement of $3^{11}/12$ inches (about 10 cm). Adult sizes start at size 1, which measures $8^7/12$ inches (22 cm). Sizes increase at intervals of $1/3$ inch (0.8 cm) a time, the length of the old barleycorn measure. (See page 32.)

American sizes may seem the same as imperial ones, but in fact they are disconcertingly larger (a British size 4, for instance, is a size $5^1/2$ in America). Continental sizes are based on a system of measures called Paris points. To work out your size in Paris points, you have to measure the length of your foot in centimetres and divide the measurement by two-thirds. Confused? You are not alone.

SATRA, the British footwear research centre in Kettering, uses its own 100-strong staff as models when trying out batches of shoes for size. They keep records of every staff member's foot measurements, so they know who to go to if they need to check a particular size. They always

John Thrupp (opposite) is a 27-year-old roofer who lives in Burton-on-Trent. He stands 6 feet 11 inches (1.8 metres) tall and he takes a staggering size 21 shoe. John says his feet weren't a problem until he was about 14, because his size seemed to correspond with his age but, after that, he just kept on growing. He has a twin brother, but he only takes a modest size 10. After John appeared on BBC's *That's Life* programme, in June 1991, someone shipped him a pair of basketball shoes from the US. 'I'd really love a pair of light canvas shoes, but whenever I call the manufacturers, they don't want to know,' he says. The problem is that no one has a shoe last big enough, so one has to be specially made. A new pair of shoes can set him back £600.

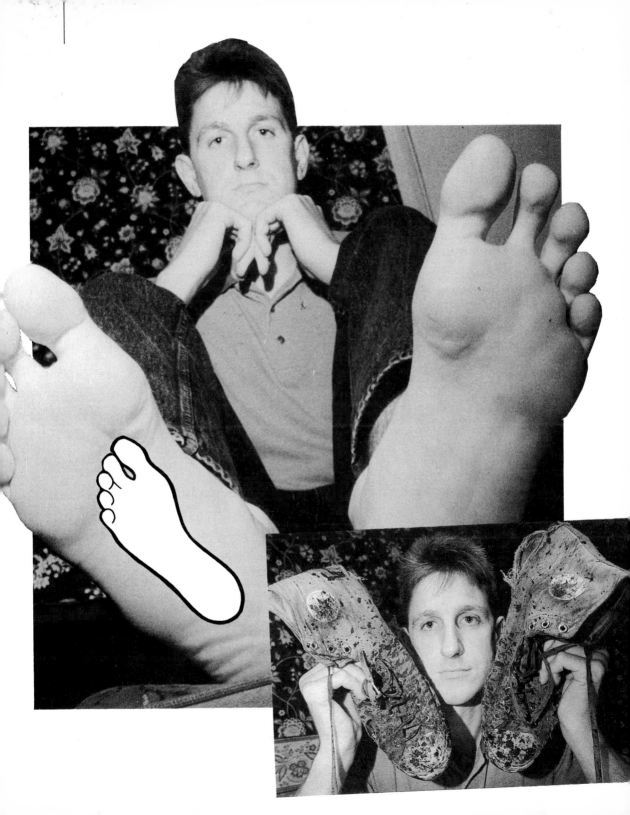

re-measure before fitting, though, because feet swell during the day, and will be larger in the afternoon than in the morning.

People who have a particular problem in buying shoes that fit will sympathise with David Cross who, for no apparent reason, has had one foot five sizes larger than the other one since birth. His mother got so exasperated at always having to throw away one half of a perfectly good pair of shoes that she started a shoe-matching service for other people in the same boat. Its name? Sole Mates.

HOW LONG IS A PIECE OF STRING? Darwin, Minnesota, is a small town in America with a big claim to fame. It is home to the world's largest ball of string – over 11 feet (3.3 metres) tall and 12 feet (3.6 metres) wide – the result of almost 30 years' collecting by a carpenter, Francis A Johnson. People have always been obsessed by the longest, widest, heaviest, richest, fastest... But why?

'Man is a competitive species whether people like it or not,' says Peter Matthews, editor of the *Guinness Book of Records*, which was set up in the 1950s to cater for exactly this enthusiasm. 'If you devote your life to something – or have a fascination for it – it's a challenge to be the best, or at least to set your own records. That's why marathon running has become so popular, because then people can set their own records.'

With global sales of well over 68 million (it has been translated into 39 languages), the *Guinness Book of Records* has earned itself an honourable mention in its own pages – as one of the world's all-time best-selling books, second only to the Bible. Surveys have shown that around half the book-buying households in the UK own at least one copy.

Francis A Johnson, of Darwin, Minnesota, began collecting odds and ends of baling twine, in 1950, simply because he did not want to throw them away. By the time he died in 1989, at the age of 85, his ball of string was so large it could only be moved by truck and trailer. Local inhabitants willingly shelled out $3 500 in removal costs to give his giant creation pride of place in the centre of town. It is now housed in a special weatherproof casing, with windows to look through. The ball's official weight, as recorded in the *Guinness Book of Records*, is 10 tons but, when it came to be weighed as part of the move, it was found to be 8.7 tons – the result, probably, of dehydration.

Getting into the book seems to be almost as popular a pastime as reading it. Peter Matthews receives thousands of claims each year, only a small proportion of which will find their way into print.

'People are always thinking that any time they do anything silly or zany it will go into the *Guinness Book of Records* and, of course, it doesn't, he said. 'We do get large numbers of claims for one-offs. But we really like to accept things that anyone can have a go at anywhere in the world.'

One of the zaniest would-be entries came from the organisers of the Swine (Sow Wrestling in the State of Nebraska) Festival. Apparently, this is an annual event in which teams wrestle with pigs, setting records for who can conquer a sow in the least time. 'They could do it every year and set their own records but, for an international book, it's a bit *too* particular,' said Mr Matthews diplomatically.

The idea for the book came after a day's shooting by the River Slaney in south-east Ireland way back in 1951. A party, led by Sir Hugh Beaver, the then managing director of Guinness, had been hunting some golden plover but they flew so fast that everyone's shots missed. That night, at dinner, they realised there were no suitable reference books to settle the question of whether or not the plover was Europe's fastest game bird. Three years later, the same question arose over grouse. Were they even faster?

Sir Hugh realised that similar arguments must be going in pubs every night. So he hit upon the idea of a book of records and commissioned Norris and Ross McWhirter to compile one. The first edition was produced in August 1955 and, well before Christmas that year, was number one on the best-seller list.

Norris McWhirter remains an editorial advisor to the

book but Peter Matthews, a self-confessed fact fanatic, is now editor. 'Many, many people are interested in extremes,' he said. 'I've been a collector of records since I was eight: I was always compiling lists of the highest mountain, longest river, number of popes…'

At first, the book was compiled mainly from written records. Now, it is an industry in its own right, and many record-breaking attempts are made for charity.

'Any achievement must be witnessed by independent people,' said Mr Matthews. 'If you had the record for the longest carrot, we would expect the witnesses to include members of botanical societies or whatever. We ask for log books, press cuttings… as much evidence as possible.'

Endurance marathons performed purely for the sake of it have been dropped. 'They became too hard, and they also became medically inadvisable. People were hallucinating. Also, if they've got a record for playing football for 80 hours or whatever, you have to ask: are they actually playing football at the end of the day, or are they just wandering around a field with a ball in the vicinity?' So, a skill element has been introduced, such as the number of scores in a 24-hour period.

'It's the problem of success that we've had to face, with lots and lots of people all over the world scouring the book,' he said. 'Records are just that. They are supreme achievements, they are not easy.'

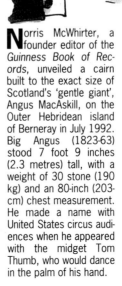

Norris McWhirter, a founder editor of the *Guinness Book of Records*, unveiled a cairn built to the exact size of Scotland's 'gentle giant', Angus MacAskill, on the Outer Hebridean island of Berneray in July 1992. Big Angus (1823-63) stood 7 foot 9 inches (2.3 metres) tall, with a weight of 30 stone (190 kg) and an 80-inch (203-cm) chest measurement. He made a name with United States circus audiences when he appeared with the midget Tom Thumb, who would dance in the palm of his hand.

THE A TO Z OF LENGTH

ACRE From the Greek *agros*, meaning field. Originally an acre was the distance a team of oxen could plough in a day. The acre is divided up into rods, poles or perches; poles are still used as a measure for allotments.

In 1824, the standard acre was set by statute at 4840 square yards (4046.7 square metres). Before then, there were numerous regional variations. In Leicestershire, for example, an acre was a measly 2308³/4 square yards (1930.3 square metres), while in generous Cheshire, it was 10 240 square yards (8561.6 square metres).

From 1994, the English acre will all but disappear, to be replaced by the European hectare, which measures 2.471 acres.

ARM A tailor who tucks a piece of cloth under his chin and holds it at arm's length is using his body as a ready measure because an arm, give or take a few inches, is 1 yard (0.9 metre) long.

BARLEYCORN In simpler, rural times, this was another handy measure. A statute of Edward II, in 1324, laid down that

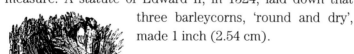

three barleycorns, 'round and dry', made 1 inch (2.54 cm).

CHAIN Land surveyors originally used the real thing, made up of 100 links and measuring 22 yards (20.1 metres). Now it survives mainly as the standard measure for a cricket pitch.

No one knows exactly why the cricket pitch is 22 yards long, any more than anyone knows why there are 11 players in a team. To seasoned cricketers, however, a slight change in measurement can spell the difference between success and failure.

Lord Orr-Ewing, the second chairman of the Metrication Board, was run out at a cricket match he organised while on holiday on Corfu in 1984. When he later queried the size of the pitch, he discovered that the original 22-yard matting wicket had worn out and been replaced with one measuring nearer 22 metres. The local supplier did not think it mattered, but the difference of some 6 feet (1.8 metres) cost Lord Orr-Ewing his wicket.

CUBIT This was an Egyptian measure, originally the length from the elbow to the middle fingertip, which is about 18 inches (45.7 cm). It was later standardised at just under 21 inches (53.3 cm). The standard was a Royal Master Cubit of black granite, and its accuracy can still be seen in the Pyramids.

DIGIT This was a subdivision of a cubit: four finger widths, or digits, made a palm, and six palms made a cubit. A seventh palm was added to make the standard. The Romans also used digits, which were reckoned as $1/16$th of a foot – $3/4$ inch (1.9 cm).

ELL An old cloth measure, now out of use, and featured in the proverb, 'Give him an inch and he'll take an ell'. In England,

Surveyors using a chain to measure a point of detail for an Ordance Survey map in the 1950s. Chains or knotted cords were used to measure distances from the 16th century onwards. In 1633 a London mathematician, Richard Norwood, set out to measure the distance from London to York by the simple process of shuffling a chain along the entire 180-mile (290-km) distance. With his chain measurements, and calculation of the angle of the sun at both ends of his journey, he calculated the latitudes of both places. It was a painful experiment but the results were surprisingly accurate.

The accuracy of Egyptian cubit measures can be seen in the Great Pyramid at Giza. Although thousands of workmen were employed in building it, the length of its sides vary by no more than 0.05 per cent.

he would be taking 1¼ yards (1.1 metres) and, in France, 1½ yards (1.3 metres).

FATHOM

Full fathom five thy father lies;
Of his bones are coral made.

(Shakespeare, *The Tempest*)

This is the stretch of a man's arms when paying out a sounding line, which has become the accepted measure of sea depth. A fathom is 6 feet (1.8 metres).

FOOT

The foot was first used by the Greeks and the Romans, although the Greek foot was smaller than the Roman one.

The French had a standard, known as the *pied du roi*, which was based on the length of Charlemagne's foot.

FURLONG A furlong measures 220 yards (201.1 metres) and was originally the length of a furrow ploughed by a team of oxen without needing a rest.

Racecourses are measured using miles, furlongs and yards, and each race has furlong markers for the last four furlongs. Flat racecourses are now measured using sophisticated infra-red measuring devices, but measuring steeplechase courses is less easy, as the path the horses take is not so direct. These are measured with a cross-country measuring wheel called the 'grass wheel'.

There are strict limits on the distance a horse can run, according to its age. A two-year-old, for example, is not allowed to run more than six furlongs (1207 metres), and a horse has to be four years old before it can enter a steeplechase.

GIRTH Based on the circumference of a man's body, a girth is 3 feet (0.9 metres).

HAND Still used as the standard measurement for horses, a hand is measured up the foreleg to the highest point on the shoulder. One hand equals 4 inches (10 cm).

Ariel (sings). Full fathom five thy father lies. . . .
Ferdinand. The ditty does remember my drown'd
father.
This is no mortal business.

Act I. Scene II.

Classes in horse shows are divided by height. Trainers will go to great lengths to get their steeds into smaller rather than larger height classes, so they stand a better chance of winning. They file the hooves, shave the withers, even set the horse's feet at an angle, so the limbs are splayed out when the horse is standing. The Joint Measuring Board are trying to standardise the process by saying that horses must be measured when standing on a special pad, with no shoes.

INCH Traditionally, the inch was the smallest measurement, hence the phrase 'inch by inch', meaning very gradually.

In the Roman Catholic Church, excommunication by inch of candle was said to give time for repentance before the final sentence was passed.

JEWISH CUBIT *Which of you by taking thought can add one cubit to his stature?* (St Matthew)

The cubit mentioned in the Bible can be taken as measuring 1 ft $9^9/_{10}$ in (55.5 cm). Goliath is described as measuring 6 cubits and a span (9 inches or 22.8 cm). Noah's Ark is said to have measured 300 x 50 x 30 cubits.

KNOT Simple measurements of speed at sea were once made by throwing a weighted rope overboard and timing how long it took the ship to travel the length of the rope. Sometimes knots were tied in the rope to make calcula-

The hand – based on the width of the human hand – is still used to measure horses. Fractions of hands are given in inches.

tions easier, which is how the word knot came to mean nautical miles per hour. One nautical mile is 6080 feet (1853 metres).

LEAGUE

Half a league, half a league,
Half a league onward.

(Tennyson, *The Charge of the Light Brigade*)

Now only a figure of speech, a league was originally three miles (4.8 kilometres).

MILE The word mile comes from the Latin, *mille*, meaning a thousand. A Roman mile was a thousand paces and was shorter than the now standard mile of 1760 yards (1609.3

metres). Milestones installed during the Roman occupation of Britain therefore give short measure by today's standards.

The old Irish and Scottish miles were a good deal longer than the standard English one: the Irish mile (still in use in country parts) was 2240 yards (2048.25 metres) and the Scottish mile was 1980 yards (1810.5 metres).

The phrase 'within a mile of an oak', which was current in the late sixteenth to eighteenth centuries, was a deliberately evasive reply to the question 'Where have you been?' Oaks were once so plentiful that most country people did live within a mile of one.

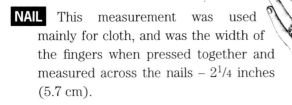

NAIL This measurement was used mainly for cloth, and was the width of the fingers when pressed together and measured across the nails – $2^1/4$ inches (5.7 cm).

OX-GANG An ox-gang was a Saxon measurement of the amount of land that could be ploughed by one ox – 15 acres (6 hectares).

PACE A pace was a Roman measurement equalling 5 feet (1.5 metres). A thousand paces made a mile (see *Mile*).

PIE-POWDER In medieval times, markets had a Court of Pie-Powder which settled measurement disputes between travelling traders and buyers. The traders were known as 'the men with dusty feet' (*pieds poudrés*), which in Franglais became pie-powder.

The mile makes a handy piece of ad-man's shorthand, as in The Miracle Mile – a stretch of Wilshire Boulevard in Los Angeles, extending 1 mile (1.6 km) from La Brea Avenue to Fairfax Avenue. The name was the idea of A W Ross, a real estate developer who was keen to promote the commercial possibilities of this piece of land in the 1930s. Miracle or not, it worked, and the area became a mecca for exclusive boutiques. Edinburgh has the Royal Mile (see picture above) – the road running from Edinburgh Castle to the Royal Palace of Holyroodhouse. London has the Square Mile, encompassing the City, and Blackpool has The Golden Mile, an action-packed section of seafront which starts to the south of Blackpool Tower. The gold-bearing reef which forms the basis of the Kalgoorlie goldfield of Western Australia is also known as the Golden Mile.

Albert Klein, who lives in Pasadena, has clocked up 1 415 844 miles (2 278 517 km) in his Volkswagen Beetle since 1963, and is still counting. He has driven to every country in Central America except Panama, and has managed over 50 000 miles (80 465 km) within Mexico alone. When he logged his one millionth mile, Volkswagen offered him a new car, but he turned the offer down and decided to go for the world record. So far he has driven through nine engines, three starter motors and 373 796 US gallons (1 414 967 litres) of petrol.

QUIRKY MEASUREMENTS In 1850, J H Alexander of Baltimore tried to compile a dictionary of the world's weights and measures, giving their equivalents in US units. He identified more than 4000 and found he was still counting...

ROD A rod measures 5¹/₂ yards (5 metres). It is called a pole or a perch in different parts of the country.

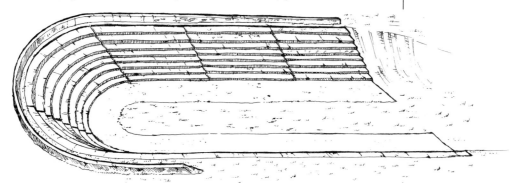

STADIUM This is the length of the original running track at Olympia in ancient Greece – 630 ft 9 in (192.27 metres). Legend has it that it was measured by Hercules as being the distance he could walk while holding his breath.

STEP A step measures half a pace – 2 ft 6 in (76 cm) (see *Pace*).

TRITHING An Anglo-Saxon term meaning one-third of a county. The Ridings of Yorkshire are a corruption of this term.

UNCIA The Roman foot was divided into 12 unciae, from which we got our inches. In the Middle Ages, the word uncial was used to describe large capital letters – originally 1 inch (2.5 cm) high – in a manuscript (see opposite).

AVLI GELII NOCTIVM ATTICARVM COM-
MENTARII.   LIBER PRIMVS.

PLVTARCHVS IN LIBRO Quem
ὁποι ψυχῶν κριν σωμάτων ἀνθρώποις πρὶ διφυίαν κρι ἀρετὴν
διαφορα: ideſt quantum inter homines animi cor
poriſque ingenio atque uirtutibus interſit : con-
ſcripſit:ſcite ſubtiliterq; rōcinatum Pythagórā
philoſophum dicit;in reperienda : modulādaq;
ſtatus longitudinis eius præſtátia . Nam quum
fere conſtaret curriculum ſtadii : quod eſt piſis
apud Iouem olympium:Herculem pedibus ſu/
is metatum:idq; feciſſe longum pedes ducétos:cætera quoq; ſtadia in ter
ris græciæ ab aliis poſtea inſtituta:pedum quidem eſſe numero ducento-
rum : ſed tamen eſſe aliquantulum breuiora:facile intellexit modum : ſpa-
tiumq; plantæ Herculis ratione proportionis habita:tanto fuiſſe:q; alioru
procerius:quanto olympicum ſtadium longius eſſet:q cætera . Compræ-
henſa autem mēſura herculani pedis ſm naturalem membroq; omnium
inter ſe copetentiam modificatus eſt.Atq; ita id collegit:quod erat conſe-
quens:tanto fuiſſe Herculem corpore excelſiorem:q alios:quanto olympicum ſtadium cæteris pari numero factis anteiret.

¶ Ab Herode attico conſulari uiro tempeſtiue deprompta in quendam
iactatum & glorioſum adoleſcentem:ſpecie tantum philoſophiæ ſectato
rem uerba Epicteti ſtoici:quibus feſtiuiter a uero ſtoico ſeiunxit uulgus
loquacium nebulonum;qui ſe ſtoicos nuncuparent.   Caput.ii.

Erodes Atticus uir & græca facundia:& conſulari honore præ
ditus:accerſebat ſæpe nos:quum apud magiſtros athenis eſſe
mus:in uillas eius urbi proximas:me & clariſſimum uiru Ser
uilianum:copluriſq; alios noſtrates : qui Roma in Græciam:
ad capiendum ingenii cultum conceſſerant.Atq; ibi tunc quum eſſemus
apud eum in uilla:cui nomen eſt cephyſia:& æſtu anni:& ſidere autumni
flagrantiſſimo propulſabamus caloris incomoda lucoq; umbra ingentiu
longis ātbulacris:& mollibus ædium poſticum refrigerantibus lauacris
nitidis:& abundis:& collucentibus:totiuſq; uillæ uenuſtate aquis;undiq;

VARIATION By the later stages of the Industrial Revolution there were more than 500 national standard units of weight and measure in Britain, with over 100 000 local variations.

In Brooklyn, US, there was a time earlier this century when city surveyors gave legal recognition to four different feet: the United States foot, the Busharistic foot, the Williamsberg foot and the foot of the 26th Ward. Some strips of Brooklyn real estate were untaxable because, after two surveys, each one made with different units, these strips had no legal existence.

WINCHESTER The Measure of Winchester was a standard established by Edgar, King of England, in the tenth century.

About two hundred years later Henry I had a yard standard made from the length of his arm, to prevent the fraudulent measuring of cloth.

In the fifteenth century Henry VII revised the yard yet again, making it the length of *his* arm – a modest 34 inches (86.3 cm). Then Elizabeth I came along and – not to be outdone by a mere short-armed man – had an extra couple of inches welded on in her name.

An octagonal bar, still to be seen in the City Museum at Winchester, shows two sovereigns' different ideas of what a yard standard should be. It has the letter H for Henry at one end and an E for Elizabeth at the other.

X The prototype for the international metre, made of platinum and iridium in the last century, had an X-shaped cross section for maximum rigidity. Copies were distributed throughout the world, with the original kept at the International Bureau of Weights and Measures in Sèvres, France. This is now redundant, since the standard for the metre is set in laboratories using measurements based on the speed of light.

YARD An early attempt at international length comparison was made in 1742, when George Graham, a Fellow of the Royal Society, took two yard bars to Paris. One was returned, inscribed with the French standard of length, the half-toise. However, there was a snag: Graham's bars were brass and the French ones were iron, and also the French had made their comparisons at different temperatures to those of the English. So, the discrepancies remained.

Metal expands in heat. A 60-foot (18.2-metre) railway line could alter about $1/2$ inch (12 mm) in length, if left free to contract and expand in winter and summer.

On 26 March 1907, the 10.52 Leeds to Newcastle train was derailed when track in a cutting was buckled into an S-shape by the heat of the sun. There had been a sharp frost the night before and the dramatic change in temperatures had been too much for the rails. Eight passengers were seriously injured and two died.

Railway track is now continuously welded with a built-in allowance for differences in temperature. Lessons from the past have been well learned.

2

This metal bar was the standard for the metre, until it was decided in the 1950s to replace it with a standard that could neither change nor be lost. Now the length of the metre can be calculated using laser beams, a process so accurate that it is the equivalent of measuring the circumference of the Earth to the nearest millimetre.

WEIGHT

O N THE ROOF of the Old Bailey, home of London's Central Criminal Court, stands the figure of Justice with a balance in her hand – a universal symbol of fair play.

The balance was the first scientific instrument to be invented, and is at least 7000 years old. Primitive weighing needed no special instruments: objects could simply be 'weighed up' by feel. However, humans make hopelessly inaccurate balances, despite having two equal arms.

Scientists prefer to talk about mass rather than weight, which varies according to gravity. A spaceman in zero gravity may be weightless, and so be able to float about, but he will still hurt himself if he bumps into the side of the spaceship. His mass, in other words, remains the same. So, this section should really be called 'Mass'... but then only those in the know would have a clue what it was all about.

WHICH WEGHS MORE: A POUND OF FEATHERS OR A POUND OF GOLD? Gold is obviously heavier than feathers, but then surely a pound is a pound, whatever it consists of. Or is it?

This giant bullion balance was made for the precious metal refiners, Brown and Brind, of Cheapside, London, in 1819. It cost £36.

This is a trick question. Gold (and also other precious metals and gems) is weighed with the troy pound, which contains only 12 ounces, so the feathers – which would be weighed with an ordinary 16-ounce pound – would be considerably heavier.

The word troy comes from the French town of Troyes, 93 miles (150 kilometres) south-east of Paris. Important fairs were held here in the Middle Ages, and the troy system of measurement was carefully controlled. The idea was to make sure people did not feel cheated, so they would keep on coming back. The avoirdupois pound, which is the imperial standard for everyday purposes, was introduced in Britain in the thirteenth century.

Both pounds are divided into ounces, which are further subdivided into drams. Fluid drams were once used to measure medicine and spirits, hence the Scots expression 'a wee dram'. For medicinal purposes only, of course!

In this represenstation from an Egyptian book of the dead, justice is dispensed by means of a balance scale. In one scale pan is a dead man's heart. In the other sits the goddess of truth and justice.

WORTH ITS WEIGHT IN GOLD Coins were originally lumps of metal, worth as much as their face value. Many of the words now used for coinage, such as the drachma, lira and pound, are also units of weight. Before abandoning it in favour of the franc, and the *Liberté, Egalité, Fraternité* of the French Revolution, France had its pound (called a *livre*), too.

The German mark is so-called from the practice of putting an official mark on weights as proof of their value, first carried out in 1042. However, the checking of weights was not always very successful. A good trade was to be had in melting down overweight coins and selling the residue metal back to the mint at a profit. In medieval Germany, possession of any kind of household scales was a punishable offence for precisely this reason.

Chiselling bits of metal from coins was also a nice little earner – and the story of coinage is the story of various attempts to foil the coin cheats. Seals were an early way of thwarting the chisellers, so they turned to clipping the edges of coins instead. This in turn led to the introduction in the seventeenth century of machine-struck coins with milled edges, but even these were not forgery-proof. One ingenious clerk, working at the Bank of England in the

St Michael.

Scales and weights have an important place in Christian iconography. St Michael (above) is frequently depicted as weighing the souls of deceased sinners.

1770s, invented a machine that could cut the milled edge off a guinea and, at the same time, put a fresh one in its place. He was eventually caught, convicted of high treason and hanged at Tyburn.

Other methods involved filing down genuine coins and soldering them on to copper discs, or making the counterfeits entirely from copper and then covering them with gold plate.

Nowadays, of course, coins are worth as much as they say they are: only mint officials would think of checking their weight. But in the days when coins were simply a handy way of paying in gold or silver, it did matter. If a merchant found a coin did not match its face value, he would be quite within his rights to demand payment by weight.

TRIAL·BY JURY The Trial of the Pyx is a timeless ritual still carried out annually by the Goldsmith's Company of the City of London. Coins of the realm are gathered in the Pyx (or mint box) and weighed to check for forgeries. The last time any were found was in 1686.

Of course, even such exacting ceremonies do not rule out other kinds of coin-cheating. Modern slot machines are by no means proof against fakes. A scandal blew up in May 1992 when a Swaziland coin that looked just like a pound, but was in fact worth only 20 pence, turned up in slot machines, parking meters and loose change all over Britain.

THE £24 000 PENNY Coins which are prized as collector's pieces can fetch sums way out of proportion to their original worth. A case in point is the 1954 penny which was sold recently for £24 000. Only one is known to have been minted but there are rumours of a second penny and coin-collectors

are eagerly hunting. Other scarce, although not unique, pennies include those minted in 1869, 1933, 1950 and 1951.

WEIGHING UP THE WEIGHTS Most people think of weights as being round, solid and made of brass but, historically, weights have come in all disguises. The Egyptians weighed gold with weights shaped like their sacred cow; the Romans used weights in the shape of vases, fruits or gods. The Ashanti, an African tribe living on the Gold Coast, used images from their everyday life. Surviving examples of figurines, which were produced up until the nineteenth century, include crocodiles, cockroaches, fish and birds. To adjust their figurines to the right weight they simply performed a painless amputation; half a leg, or even an entire one, could be cut off in the interests of balance.

The stone as a unit of weight derives from an actual stone – and inevitably originally differed from region to

In the ancient ceremony of the Trial of the Pyx, which dates back to 1248 or earlier, jurors from the Goldsmith's Company of London sit in judgment on coins made by the Royal Mint. Coins from Britain and the Commonwealth are weighed and checked for diameter and composition. The juror's verdicts are later given to the Queen's Remembrancer, in the presence of the Chancellor of the Exchequer or his deputy. Pictured above, the 1982 trial showing Dr Jeremy Gerhard, Deputy Master of the Mint, talking to The Queen as members of the jury count gold coins in the Livery Hall.

region. The British stone that remains is divided into 14 lb, and is used only for weighing humans. A weight known as a clove, which was about half a stone, was once used for weighing wool and cheese.

Then, of course, there is the hundredweight. In 1821, when John Quincy Adams, then the American Secretary of State, was casting around for a particularly horrible example of the abuse of the English language, he hit upon this one – the hundredweight is not a hundred of anything, but actually 112 lb.

It is all thanks to Edward I, apparently, who for some obscure reason decreed that the 'true hundredweight' of 100 lb should become 112 lb – with an interim weight of 108 lb, just so people could get used to the idea.

Even seven centuries later, no one is used to the idea but, with metrication just around the corner, it doesn't matter very much.

AN HONEST POUND In the bad old days, merchants would often use one pound-weight when they bought goods and another, lighter but identical in name, when they sold them. Standardising the pound and its fellow weights was a ruling concern of British sovereigns from earliest times. In 1357, Edward III ordered a set of official weights and balances to be sent to all the sheriffs of England. Elizabeth I ordered an official investigation into weights which lasted for six years. Existing weights were destroyed and replaced by the new standards in 1588. These held sway until Victorian times.

In 1824, a commission of the great and the good set a new standard for the pound and gave detailed directions for

its restoration, should anything happen to it. As we know from the story of the yard, something did happen to it. The fire at the Houses of Parliament came just 10 years after the commission had made its deliberations, and it soon became obvious that their formula for restoring it was scientific pie in the sky.

The idea had been to weigh a cubic inch of distilled water at a set temperature and pressure, and from this to calculate a value for the pound. But the team of scientists appointed to tackle the task decided there must be an easier way. Next time, they concluded, they would simply make plenty of copies so no one would have to go through the same tortuous business again.

At the head of the team was W H Miller, Professor of Mineralogy at the University of Cambridge. He took his responsibilities very seriously, writing an exhaustive account of his labours in the 1856 volume of *Philosophical Transactions of the Royal Society of London*. His article, called 'On the Construction of the New Imperial Standard Pound, and its Copies of Platinum', occupies some 200 pages. Three-quarters of these are simply tables of numbers.

These weights, produced in the reign of Elizabeth I, bear the letters EL as the seal of royal approval. They were not superseded until 1824.

Philosophical Transactions (the word 'philosophy' is used here to mean science) was the official journal of the Royal Society. Copies were sent out free to foreign members in all corners of the Empire, from Madras to Barbados. A quick glance at the pages of the 1856 volume shows just how much was going on in science at this time.

The first article is entitled 'On the Constitution and Properties of Ozone'. This is followed by 'Some Observations on the Ova of the Salmon: an open letter to Charles Darwin from the Inspector-General of Army Hospitals'; 'Experimental Research in Electricity – Thirtieth Series' by Michael Faraday; Professor Owen the dinosaur-hunter on the skull of the megatherium; and the Rev. J Challis, Plumian Professor of Astronomy and Experimental Philosophy at the University of Cambridge on 'The Problem of the Three Bodies'. Bodies here means planets rather than corpses, and it is clearly a knotty problem, to be solved only by wading through 23 pages of mathematical formulae.

W H Miller's work on the imperial pound obviously had the necessary scientific gravitas and a new standard, with four copies as disaster insurance, was finally approved in 1855. A platinum cylinder with a groove around the top so it could be lifted up with an ivory fork, the original parliamentary standard is now preserved in the National Physical Laboratory at Teddington in Middlesex. Sadly, considering the amount of work that went into its manufacture, it is of historical interest only. The pound is now defined by its relationship to another lump of metal – the kilogram.

Small amounts of precious stones are measured in carats. Once there were many different carats but, at the beginning of the twentieth century, the weight was standardised at 0.20 grams. The Star of Africa (above), the world's largest cut diamond, is 530.2 metric carats in weight.

THE KILO AND ITS WEIGHT PROBLEM The kilogram was originally called the kilograve – grave meaning heavy, as in gravity – but was renamed when the gram came into use as a unit of weight. Like the metre, the kilogram was a child of the French Revolution (pictured right) and, also like the metre, its birth was attended with political difficulties.

Experiments to determine its weight were carried out by René Just Hauy (1743-1822) – a founder of the science of crystallography – and the chemist, Antoine Laurent Lavoisier (1743-94). However, Lavoisier's brilliance as a chemist was only partly appreciated by his contemporaries. His tricky social position as one of the aristocratic farmers-general led to his downfall at the hands of the revolutionaries. He was guillotined in 1794, five years before the metric system he had helped to create came into being.

The original measurements for the kilo involved determining the density of water – the same method that was supposedly used later for the Victorian replacement of the pound. After the kilo had been in use for a few years, scientists found this was not such an accurate way of measuring after all, so they abandoned the idea of a natural standard and redefined the weight of the kilo as the weight of the original block.

Other standards of weight and measure are now expressed in terms of physical constants such as the speed of light, but, to this day, the standard for the kilo is a lump of metal. Le Grand K is a platinum-iridium cylinder which is kept in three glass domes in a vault in the International Bureau of Weights at Sèvres, near Paris. And, much to the alarm of scientists, recent measurements suggest that it may be shrinking.

Copies of the kilogram, which are called witnesses, are distributed throughout the world. When the kilo's custodians recalled the witnesses to check their weights, they discovered that six out of seven were slightly heavier than the original. If the kilo is shrinking, it is only by 75 billionths of a kilo, which is less than the weight of a grain of sand. Scientists think the problem could lie in an emery paste polish that was used, but even so they are worried. Even such an infinitesimal variation could make a difference in calculations where precision is vital.

If you fill a series of milk bottles with different levels of water, making sure the sides are not touching, you can play them, like a xylophone, using a stick. The fuller the bottle, the deeper the sound. Traditional Chinese measurement used this principle for measuring volume by sound.

A SOUND SYSTEM OF MEASUREMENT Take a series of milk-bottles, fill them with different levels of water and tap the sides with a stick. Hey presto – an instant xylophone!

In China, exactly this principle was used to establish standards of volume. Containers for grain and wine were defined not only by weight but also by sound: given a uniform shape and weight, only a correctly-filled container will sound the right pitch when struck. In old Chinese the same word was used for wine bowl, grain measure and bell.

Antoine Laurent Lavoisier with his artist wife, as painted by Jacques Louis David. Often called the father of modern chemistry, Lavoisier played a vital part in the measurements taken to determine the weight of the kilogram, but he did not live to see the results of his work. Like many others of his class and time, he met a violent death at the hands of the 'machine' – otherwise known as the guillotine.

ffortaller and regratof markett and bey res and vitelars

CHECKING OUT THE CHEATS

Thou shalt not have in thine house divers measures, a great and a small.

But thou shalt have a perfect and just weight, a perfect and just measure shalt thou have: that thy days may be lengthened in the land which the Lord thy God giveth thee.

Deuteronomy, Ch. 25 v. 14-15

Let there be one measure of wine throughout our whole realm; and one measure of ale; and one measure of corn, to wit, 'the London quarter'; and one width of cloth (whether dyed, or russet, or halberget), to wit, two yards

This early engraving, dated 1496, shows King Henry VII presiding over a trial of weights and measures. In the foreground, unjust measures are being consigned to the flames. From Magna Carta on, sovereigns realised that a fair system of weights and measures was vital in keeping the populace happy.

within the selvedges; of weights also let it be as of measures.

Magna Carta, 1215

From the Bible to Magna Carta, the writing was on the wall for short-measure merchants. And that included royalty, who had an unfortunate tendency to collect taxes under one measure and use another, lighter one, when paying out money.

In France, during the troubled years after the Revolution, one of the reasons the metric system was so slow to be adopted was the lack of public scales for people to check their purchases. It led to a suspicion that the whole idea was one giant con, and so forced Napoleon to back-pedal and allow the old medieval measures to continue alongside the new metric ones.

In New York at the turn of the century, 'honest weight' became a popular political slogan, thanks to the efforts of one tough Irishman, Patrick Derry. Within 12 months of being appointed head of the city's Bureau of Weights and Measures in 1906, he and his men had inspected 200 000 measuring instruments. There were many grumbles from merchants, not least because the Bureau exposed some of their pet tricks. One poultry dealer had been weighing chickens stuffed with padlocks, while another merchant had been placing lumps of putty beneath the scale pans. Scales had bent pointers and, in one case, the pointer was attached to a hidden string leading to a foot pedal.

The following year in Chicago, the Women's Full Weight Club got their own back on local merchants who had short-changed them over the years. They built a huge bonfire on the shores of Lake Michigan, and burned the confiscated scales and other measuring instruments.

THE BAKER'S DOZEN

Bread has always been a symbolic peasant staple, so it is not surprising that bakers should have come under particular scrutiny from the fair weight lobby. The baker's dozen came into being under regulations which required bakers to supply 13 loaves to the dozen, in case any of them were underweight.

The Statute Concerning Bakers and Brewers, introduced in 1266, laid down punishment in the stocks for bakers giving short weight. It was a punishment 'which shall not be remitted to the offender either for gold or silver'.

After 1836, bakers in Britain were obliged by law to supply scales and weights in their shops and on travelling carts, and to weigh loaves if asked to do so. This perpetuated the idea of the baker's dozen. Bread was bound to lose moisture, and therefore weight, when it had travelled in a cart all day, so loaves had to be baked overweight to allow for subsequent evaporation. Bread no longer has to be weighed on request in Britain, but it is a relatively recent dispensation. Carts were exempted in 1926, but until 1964 bakeries still had to use scales.

Various Weights and Measures Acts lay down rules of sale in minute detail. Certain products, such as butter, potatoes, some cereals, jam and dried lentils, have to be sold in set quantities if they are pre-packed, to make price comparisons easier. Pre-packed fresh fruit and vegetables have to be sold within sight of a prominently displayed set of scales, so customers can check what they're getting. Trading Standards Officers, who are the old Weights and Measures Inspectors under a new name, spend a lot of time simply explaining the regulations to bewildered shopkeepers.

World-famous opera singer, Luciano Pavarotti, who once weighed 20 stone (127 kg), has been on some much-publicised diets to help him negotiate opera house stairs better.

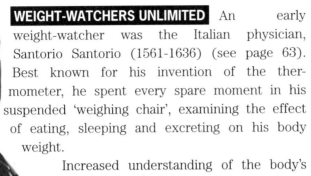

WEIGHT-WATCHERS UNLIMITED An early weight-watcher was the Italian physician, Santorio Santorio (1561-1636) (see page 63). Best known for his invention of the thermometer, he spent every spare moment in his suspended 'weighing chair', examining the effect of eating, sleeping and excreting on his body weight.

Increased understanding of the body's metabolism has led modern weight-watchers to attach enormous importance to the weighing out of foods. Weight Watchers International – one of the few clubs you *have* to be overweight to join – has menu plans in which even the amount of salad cream (two teaspoons only) is specified.

Overweight and obesity are the two most common nutritional disorders in the UK today, giving rise to more ill-health than all the vitamin deficiencies combined; as many as 45 per cent of men and 36 per cent of women are overweight. Dieting verges on a national obsession but, judging by the constant re-appearance of diet books on the best-seller lists, not many people do it effectively.

Weight Watchers was founded in New York by Jean Nidetch in 1963,

There are 17 000 angling competitions every year in Britain, and the result of each one depends entirely on weight. For a world record to be approved, the fish has to be kept for inspection by independent experts. Steve Sharpe, (above right), a coalman from Newport, Isle of Wight, recently caught a giant ling weighing 21 lb 4 oz (9.6 kg) but, never having seen a ling before, he thought it was a conger. It was only after he had made a meal of his catch that he found he had eaten a potential world record. His fish was 1 lb 12 oz (0.7 kg) above the current British best, but he had only the bones of his triumph to show for it.

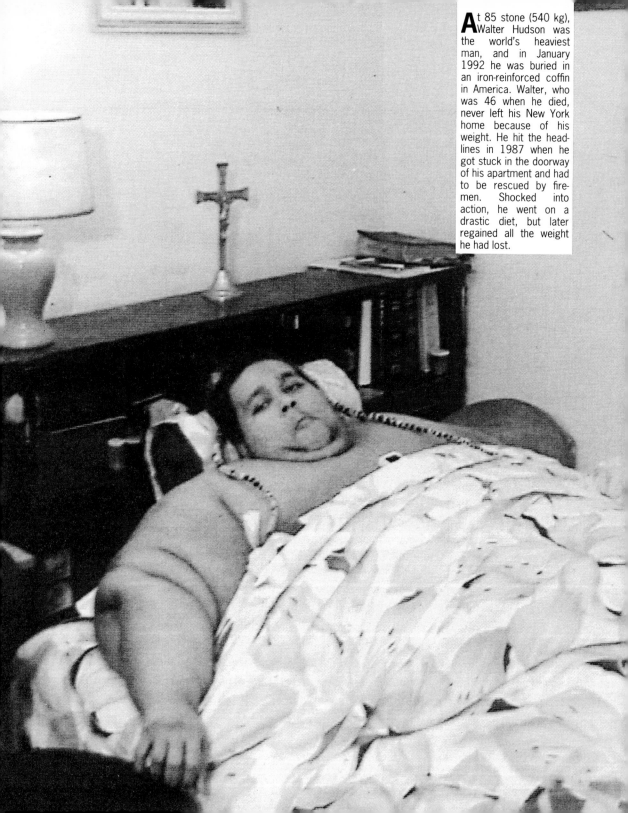

At 85 stone (540 kg), Walter Hudson was the world's heaviest man, and in January 1992 he was buried in an iron-reinforced coffin in America. Walter, who was 46 when he died, never left his New York home because of his weight. He hit the head-lines in 1987 when he got stuck in the doorway of his apartment and had to be rescued by fire-men. Shocked into action, he went on a drastic diet, but later regained all the weight he had lost.

and now helps slimmers in 24 different countries. The first Weight Watchers class in the UK was held in Datchet, near Windsor, in 1967. There are now over 3000 classes held countrywide each week. Anyone over the age of 10 can join, provided they have at least 10 lb (4.5 kg) to shed.

The most potent force in this and other schemes like it is the sort of benign moral blackmail that comes from belonging to a group. There are structured eating plans, but discussions leading to a degree of self-knowledge also help people to achieve their 'goal' weight.

Psychiatrists working with people who have eating disorders have found that many women have a totally distorted body image. Dr Jane Wardle, a self-image specialist at the Institute of Psychiatry in London, has carried out experiments which involve measuring people's body width with calipers, then asking them how wide they think they are. (She puts her subjects – mostly women – in a darkened room, then asks them to estimate their width from sets of lights.) Oddly enough, most women think they are wider than they actually are, but underestimate their real weight.

Many models border on the anorexic. One model agency quotes the average weight of a 5 ft 11 in (1.8 metres) fashion model as 8 st 6 lb (53.5 kg) – about 2 stone (12.7 kg) underweight, according to most standard height/weight charts. Yet although scientists generally agree on an optimum weight range, calculated by setting weight against height and bone structure, they do not agree that there is such a thing as a natural weight.

The idea of natural weight is that the body has a certain weight which it is programmed to maintain; whatever weird eating patterns or lifestyle the body's owner follows, the body will adjust its metabolism accordingly. It is an idea that has gained wide currency in the United States, but some British scientists think it is just a lot of hooey.

Meanwhile some American feminists, enraged at the tyranny of dieting, have taken to the streets in protest. Their slogan? 'Scales are for fish, not women.'

Jockeys can go to extreme lengths to lose weight in time for a race. Flat racer, Bruce Raymond reckons he can lose up to 5 lbs in two hours by jumping up and down in a sauna. 'I duck my head in and out of a bucket of cold water so that I can bear being in there,' he says. 'You don't want to be under the target weight, though, because you'll feel weak.'

THE OXFORD GOBSTOPPER   If measuring is important in dieting, it is even more so in cooking. Cookery writer Prue Leith once wrote a recipe in the *Daily Mail* for Oxford marmalade in which she specified two tablespoons of black treacle. An unfortunate misprint rendered the abbreviation 'tbs' as 'lbs' – and the newspaper's switchboard was jammed with complaints about the gooey mess which ensued.

One person calculated you would need to make 57 lb (25.8 kg) of marmalade to accommodate 2 lb (0.9 kg) of treacle. Another simply sent her teeth – and a dentist's bill – in the post.

Santorio Santorio per-
formed some of the
earliest experiments in
metabolism in this
weighing chair. He dis-
covered that even just
by sweating people can
lose weight. Jockeys fol-
low this principle to
reach the right weight in
time for a race, and can
lose up to half a stone
(3 kg) simply by wearing
a sweat suit in a sauna.
Bruce Raymond has an
optimum riding weight of
8 stone 5 lb (53 kg),
which means he has to
weigh 8 stone 2 lb (51
kg) stripped (after allowing for the weight of his
equipment). He weighs
himself about 10 times a
day, which apparently is
quite normal for a jockey.

TIME

At midnight, Cinderella's coach becomes a pumpkin, and her glad rags turn to shreds. At midnight, according to the Chicago-based *Bulletin of The Atomic Scientists*, the world will self-destruct. The nuclear Doomsday Clock, designed in 1947 by the wife of a physicist who worked on the first atomic bomb, charts the world's movement towards nuclear holocaust. Since its first appearance on the front cover of the bulletin, it has been changed 14 times. At the height of the Cold War in the 1960s, the hands stood at two minutes to midnight. With the recent break-up of the Soviet Union, and greater optimism about the nuclear future, it now stands at 17 minutes to midnight.

From dawn to dusk, certain times of day have always been symbolic, but the obsession with accurate timekeeping is a relatively recent one. 'Time rules life' is the motto of the National Association of Watch and Clock Collectors. And so it does.

TEMPUS FUGIT This Roman maxim (meaning 'time flies') actually refers to the flight of clouds overhead – to the weather, and only indirectly to time. The word 'time' is

The Doomsday Clock ... midnight as Armageddon. The hands retreated from global war in the December 1991 issue of the Chicago-based *Bulletin of The Atomic Scientists*, when they were put back 7 minutes, to stand at their new time of 17 minutes to midnight. Before this optimistic move, the furthest away from midnight they had stood was in 1963. The hands were then set at 11.48 to reflect the signing of a partial test ban treaty by the United States and the Soviet Union.

related to the Anglo-Saxon *tid*, meaning the season or the hour (as in 'Time and tide wait for no man'.)

The need for people to know what time of year it was came when our ancestors first moved from being hunter-gatherers to farmers. *Works and days*, written by the Greek poet Hesiod, who lived in 8 BC, was an early oral calendar. Originally belted out like a ballad to the accompaniment of a lyre, it told people exactly when to do things. Only those who picked their grapes at the right time, it implied, would get on in life; just like those bullying gardening columnists who tell you when to sow the beans.

The Sioux Indians of Dakota had picture charts which served both as calendars and communal memories. Thus the winter of 1762-3 was remembered by a prairie fire which destroyed their camp; 1800-1 was the winter when nine white men came to trade; and 1801-2 was the winter when a trader brought the first guns. Other incidents were simply remembered by their relationship to these key events.

Today, despite the fact that we are surrounded by calendars and timepieces of every description, people rarely remember events by date or time. They are more likely to use personal recollections as ways to jog their memories. It might be 'The year I got a new Filofax for Christmas', rather than 'The year we shot the most buffalo', but the principle remains the same.

OUR DAYS ARE NUMBERED The Sumerians (the world's first urban civilisation, who lived about 2500 BC) were the first people to divide a year into days, and days into hours, and the Ancient Egyptians built on that tradition. The oldest known astronomical texts were found on the lids of wooden coffins dating from the Ninth Dynasty (about 2150 BC). The dead, they believed, needed to be able to tell the time as well as the living.

Our calendar is based on that of the Romans, and dates back to 300 BC. Various bits of juggling since then mean we now have a calendar accurate to within one day in 44 000 years.

Originally, the Romans had a 120-day year, based on the lunar cycle and divided into four months – Martius, Aprilis, Maisis and Junius. When Julius Caesar came to

The Italian composer, Gioacchino Rossini, born on 29 February 1792, was one of the more famous leap-year babies. Leap years have been part of the calendar for over 2000 years, which has given plenty of time for a clutch of myths and legends to grow up around them. The Rhinelanders in Germany used to believe that a baby born on 29 February would be clairvoyant, but haunted by evil spirits throughout his or her life. There is also, of course, the tradition of leap-year proposals. The custom is said to date back to St Patrick who, after a riot at a nunnery run by St Bridget, agreed to allow the girls to pop the question to the man of their choice in leap years. The need for a leap year arises from the fact that the Earth does not take exactly 365 days to go round the sun. It actually takes 365 days, 5 hours, 48 minutes and 45.9747 seconds. In the Julian calendar, introduced by Julius Caesar, every fourth year is a leap year. This was further refined by Pope Gregory, who laid down that end-of-the-century years are only leap years if they can be divided by four. So 1900 was not a leap year – but 2000 will be.

power, however, he found that the calendar didn't synchronise with the seasons, so he decreed that year 46 should last 445 days – and introduced the 365-day year from 45 BC onwards. The new calendar was to be based on the movements of the sun, with a leap year every four years – almost the same as today. It was known as the Julian calendar.

The idea of building a calendar around the sun had existed since the ancient Egyptians, who also had a 365-day year, but this had somehow been forgotten in the interim. Most other early calendars had been based on the moon, which takes roughly $27^{1}/2$ days to circle the earth. But, of course, the seasons depend on the sun.

Julius Caesar's sequence of months was impeccably logical, with alternate months of 30 and 31 days, except for February. Unfortunately, the whole system was thrown into confusion after his death by one man – Caesar's great-nephew, who assumed power and eventually became the Emperor Augustus.

It is Augustus's fault that every schoolchild has to learn that impossible rhyme, 'Thirty days hath September...' because he wrecked Julius Caesar's carefully planned scheme by demanding that the month named after Augustus – August – should have 31 days, not 30. After all, Julius Caesar's month – July – had 31 days, so why couldn't he have the same? The mess his egocentricity made of the calendar has continued for two thousand years.

In the sixteenth century, the calendar once again underwent a carefully-planned change under Pope Gregory XIII. Easter

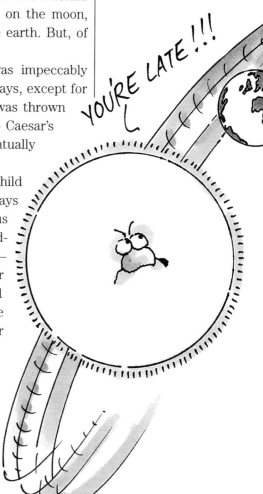

YOU'RE LATE !!!

had been falling later and later in the year, and a Papal Order was issued in 1582 which eliminated 11 days during that October to put matters right. However, because it was a Roman Catholic reform, it was regarded with great suspicion by Protestants. Britain didn't adopt this new Gregorian calendar until 1752, and even then the idea of 'losing' 11 days overnight was not popular. (People thought their lifespans would be reduced by 11 days.) Several were killed in riots in Bristol after the unilateral declaration that the day after 4 September would be 14 September. New Year's Day was also changed from 25 March to 1 January.

The Russians didn't adopt the Gregorian calendar until the revolution of 1917.

THE FRENCH REPUBLICAN CALENDAR In 1792, during the French Revolution, a new calendar, severing all connections with the past, was introduced to celebrate the new French republic. From 1792 onwards, the years were to be numbered in Roman – Anno I, Anno II, and so on – with every four-year period being called a Franciade. There would be 12 months of 30 days each, with 5 days tacked on to the end of the year.

Because the new calendar was supposed to symbolise the dawn of a new republican era, every reminder of Christianity was removed. Saints' days, feast days and even Sundays were all consigned to the dustbin of history. So, too, were the Roman emperors and gods who had given their names to the old months.

Instead, the months were given names to suit the time of year in which they fell. The dramatic poet Fabre d'Eglantine was asked to think up names that were suitably poetic, but his flowery prose didn't translate too well, so

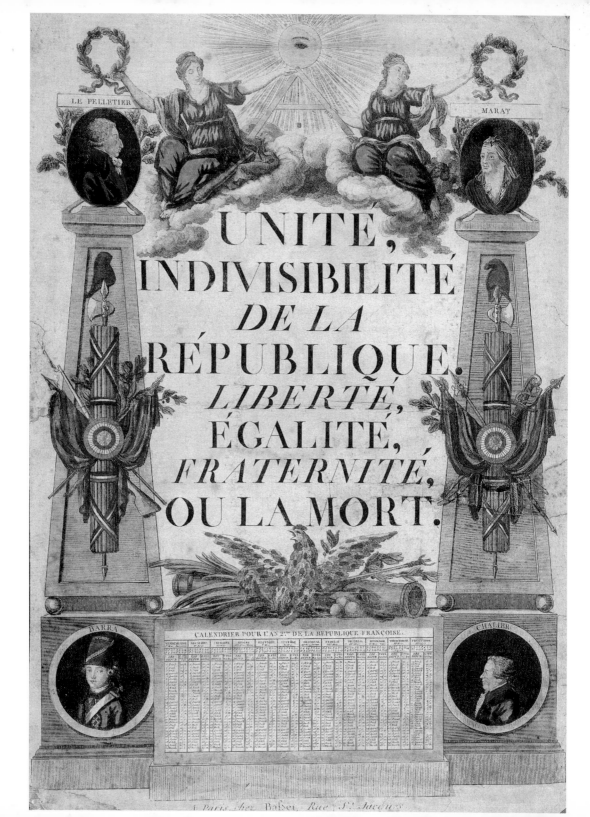

LE PELLETIER

MARAT

UNITÉ,
INDIVISIBILITÉ
DE LA
RÉPUBLIQUE.
LIBERTÉ,
ÉGALITÉ,
FRATERNITÉ,
OU LA MORT.

BARRA

CHALIER

CALENDRIER POUR L'AN 2.me DE LA RÉPUBLIQUE FRANÇOISE.

A Paris chez Basset, Rue St. Jacques.

English cynics provided their own translations – Slippy, Nippy, Drippy, Wheezy…

The first month which, predictably, began on 22 September, the day the Republic was founded, was to be called Vendémiaire, after the *vendange*, or wine harvest. This was followed by Brumaire, the misty month, Frimaire, the cold month, and so on. The end of the year consisted of five days of holiday, dubbed sans-culottides after the peasants, and dedicated to Virtue, Talent, Labour, Opinion and Rewards. Leap years were to have an extra day dedicated to the Revolution, to be marked by a great Olympic-style games.

Most revolutionary of all, however, was the introduction of the 10-day week, the 10-hour day, the 100-minute hour and the 100-second minute. The new week, or *décade*, meant nine days of hard labour before one day of rest. Could this be why the new calendar lasted a mere 13 years? In fact, the attempt to redivide the day fizzled out long before the new calendar. The French did not take kindly to the life of deci-man, and decimal time-keeping had been abandoned by 1795.

The calendar also became a mere curiosity of history when the new emperor, Napoleon, ditched it in exchange for recognition of his authority from the Pope. From 1 January 1806, the French were given back their saints' days, feast days and Sundays.

OTHER REVOLUTIONARY CALENDARS However, that was not the end of attempts to tinker with the calendar. The French philosopher, Auguste Comte (1798-1857), decided that the calendar should provide a model to show the evolution of

This decimal watch is a rare survival of the attempt to impose deci-time on the French people. A French Revolutionary fob watch, it shows the 10 hours of the day alongside the old 24-hour system it tried to replace.

Opposite: Calender for Year II of the French Republic (1793/4), decorated with revolutionary heroes and the tricolour.

humanity. He proposed adding an extra month to the existing 12 and renaming them all. The months were to be called Moses, Homer, Aristotle, Archimedes, Caesar, St Paul, Charlemagne, Dante, Gutenberg, Shakespeare, Descartes, Frederick II and Bichat. Bichat, incidentally, was a French anatomist.

Comte's weeks were also named after histori-  cal figures, ranging from Buddha to Newton, and his days were also renamed. Altogether, he came up with a total of 559 new names, covering a 3000-year time span. What successive generations were supposed to do when new candidates for such an honour emerged, history doesn't relate. Anyway, it is an academic question – Comte's calendar never left the written page.

In the 1920s, the idea of a new World Calendar gained some currency in the League of Nations but, again, it never left the drawing board.

Simplest of all the League of Nations solutions came from a Mr Stijepo-Ferri of the then Kingdom of the Serbs, Croats and Slovenes. Why not, he asked, simply abolish the whole idea of months and number the days from 1 to 365 (or 366)? Why not, indeed.

NATURAL CLOCKS Primitive people had no calendars or clocks, but they didn't really need them. Early farmers learnt to tell the seasons simply by looking at the stars. In Ancient Egypt, there was an additional indicator – the annual flooding of the Nile.

The moon was effectively the first chronometer. Ancient Middle Eastern astronomers would climb a mountain and wait for the moon to rise to see if it was the start of a new month, or just the last day of the old one. The sun was also a vital time-keeper. The earliest known solar clock was found in Egypt, dated 1500 BC. Shaped like a T-square, it measured the day in two halves from dawn to midday, and midday to dusk.

Different civilisations had different ideas about when the day started. For the Egyptians, it started at dawn, while for the Babylonians, Jews and Muslims, it started at dusk (which is why their traditional religious fast days begin at this time). The problem with counting days from dusk or dawn is that the length of each day then differs according to the seasons. So, the Romans came up with the idea of starting the day at midnight.

One of the most efficient clocks – with no mechanical parts to go wrong – is the human body. It is usually accurate to the nearest hour, but it only works in the presence of normal patterns of day and night. Put someone in a room with the light constantly on and they will become totally disorientated. They may think they have been awake for longer than they actually have, and start worrying about not getting enough sleep.

Anyone who has suffered from jet lag will know that you may feel fine during the day, but when the sun goes down, the body will fight back with the urge to return to its natural or circadian rhythm.

Most organisms have their own circadian rhythm (from the Latin, *circa* 'about', *dies* 'day'), although its length may vary from 23 to 27 hours. The human circadian clock not only

The experience of twentieth-century hostages shows that the old ways of telling time still hold good – provided the captive has light and dark to do it with. Those kept blindfold quickly lose all track of time. Ex-fighter pilot, Jackie Mann (right), taken hostage in Beirut in May 1989, was kept chained up like a dog in a bare room for 865 days. For most of that time, he could see outside, and he told the time by the shadows thrown by a fig tree – and marked off the days on a calendar scratched on a wall. When he was released on 24 September 1991, he was only two weeks out in his reckoning.

tells the body when to wake up and when to sleep, but regulates the body temperature and releases hormones.

What controls the clock is a mystery that has exercised students of chronobiology (a branch of physiology) over the past decade.

'A SAD TALE'S BEST FOR WINTER' So said Shakespeare in *The Winter's Tale*, and most people do feel a bit gloomy as the nights draw in and the weather gets colder. In some people, however, the gloom becomes a clinical condition. SAD – or Seasonal Affective Disorder – is a depression which occurs in the winter and was only recognised in the mid 1980s.

No one has yet proved conclusively what causes it, but one of the most likely factors seems to be the disruption of the body clock by the shortened days of autumn and winter. Many psychiatrists claim dramatic improvements on patients who are treated with nothing more sophisticated than regular doses of light. Biologists at Harvard University in the United States have shown that it is perfectly possible to re-set the human body clock by using artificial light, and the idea of using light to overcome jet lag has met with some success.

Besides its daily rhythms, the body clock also ticks in time with the weeks, and the months. The female menstrual cycle lasts approximately one month, being anything between 21 and 35 days long. In fact, the 'textbook' menstrual cycle of 28 days coincides almost exactly with the length of the moon's cycle, from one new moon to the next. In French, the connection is made explicit with their phrase for it: *'le moment de la lune'*. The Maori call it 'moon sickness', and the Papuans believe that the moon has intercourse with girls, and that is the cause of their periods.

Women who live or work together often find that their menstrual cycles coincide. No one knows exactly why this is, but it is thought to be related to pheronomes – chemical substances secreted by our bodies which have a subtle but definite effect on other people. Unconsciously picking up these invisible physical messages, women's bodies start to march in time.

The menstrual cycle also seems to be crucial in the timing of operations for breast cancer. Tests and studies carried out at Guy's Hospital in London by Ian Fentiman, deputy director of the Imperial Cancer Research Fund, have shown that the second half of a woman's menstrual cycle is the best time for such operations. Higher levels of the female hormone progesterone make the cancer cells cohesive and easier to remove during surgery. It is like the difference between picking up a shelled hard-boiled egg and a raw one.

In the Middle Ages, medical students had to study astronomy to predict the best time to operate on patients. Perhaps they knew more than we think.

On 9 November 1965, New York suffered an overwhelming blackout. Nine months later, hospital records showed a bulge in the number of births. Headlines of the nudge, nudge, wink, wink variety proclaimed the news. Closer examination, however, showed that this bulge was actually normal for that time of year. Just as animals have their breeding season so, it seems, do humans. A Dutch survey has shown that the highest conception rate is in the spring, with a lower peak in the autumn. Biorhythms rule.

TIME ON THEIR HANDS Primitive sundials were often no more than a stick rammed in the ground. The idea may have come from watching the shadows cast by trees at different times of the day.

Sundials have two major flaws. First, the sun moves at different speeds at different times of year, leaving a fairly generous margin for error. Second, and most obviously, a sundial can only work when the sun is shining.

The Babylonians got round the first problem by dividing the day and night into 24 units – lines showing these Babylonian hours can still be seen on sundials today. The second problem, of telling the time in darkness or gloomy weather, was solved by inventing other methods. The Romans had what was effectively the first speaking clock – a man in the forum who shouted out the noon hour. The water clock, or clepsydra, as the Greeks called it, was known to the ancient Egyptians.

In the Tower of the Winds, the ruins of which can still be seen in Athens, the Greeks brought together sundials, a windvane and a huge, complicated water clock. It had a revolving float which not only marked the time inside the slowly filling chamber, but also simulated the rotation of the planets.

The Roman writer Juvenal (AD 50-150) wrote about rich people who had private water clocks and slaves who read out the time. The first public clepsydra appeared in Rome in 158 BC, and they were also introduced into courts, to limit speech lengths. Lawyers were said to bribe the

Clocks and other time-pieces have been used to set limits on eloquence since Roman times. Preachers used to time their sermons with an hourglass and, in the British House of Commons, the 10-Minute Rule enables MPs to bring in bills which would otherwise never see the light of day. These are usually just a way of making a political point, rather than serious attempts at legislation. The 10-Minute Rule allows for one brief speech for the motion, and another against, to be made in the House after Prime Minister's Question Time. It is a prime spot, and much fought over, as the House is likely to be full, with good television and newspaper coverage. There is rarely time for debate, but these bills do sometimes become law if they are not contentious. About 25 have gone on to receive the Royal Assent since the war.

READY…STEADY·

clepsydra attendant to regulate the water supply in their favour. (In the British House of Commons today, a clock is kept in the chamber to limit MPs' speeches on bills introduced under the 10-Minute Rule. The clock, however, can't be bribed.)

China made major advances in clock-making in the eleventh century. A Chinese mandarin, Su Sung (1020-1101), designed a mechanical water clock which some experts reckon to have been more accurate than the first European clocks, even though they were produced over two centuries later. Sadly, the technical expertise died with its Chinese makers, and since only a written description of the clock exists, no one will ever know exactly how accurate it was. Su Sung was not a professional clock-maker, nor were his assistants. In fact his chief designer and supervisor of construction was apparently a minor ministry official.

The clock, which was housed in a tower about 40 feet (12 metres) high, was designed to reproduce the movements of the

The Pelican Sundial, first erected in 1579, makes a striking centrepiece in the front quadrangle of Corpus Christi College, Oxford. Crowned by a golden pelican, symbolising Christ's sacrifice, it shows just how elaborate sundials can be. There are coats of arms (including those of the House of Tudor and the University of Oxford), Latin mottoes and complicated tables of letters and numerals. There is a table for finding the time by moonlight, and another for finding the date of movable and fixed feasts, including the Oxford and law terms. The sundial also has charts showing the signs of the zodiac, and lines marking both the Babylonian and equinoctial hours. The Babylonian hours, which divided the time between sunrise and sunset into 12 equal parts, were considerably shorter in winter than in summer. So, by the sixteenth century, they were being superseded by the more uniform equinoctial hours, which are still in use today. They are called equinoctial because, on the days of the equinoxes, the hours of daylight and night are equal.

1581 EST DEO GRATIA

sun, moon and selected stars. A series of rotating rings represented the paths of these bodies as seen from earth. Shafts and cogs were linked to a revolving inner tower, which used placards to show the time. The whole device was powered by a giant wooden water-wheel.

It was a complicated mechanism, whose sophistication was apparently lost on the star-gazing Chinese – they were more interested in it as an aid to astrological divination than as an accurate timepiece. Their main concern seems to have been plotting the positions of the stars when the Emperor's wives or concubines gave birth, so they could calculate the babies' horoscopes.

When Jesuit missionaires visited China five centuries later, no trace remained of this elaborate clock. Indeed, Chinese rulers fell upon the mechanical clocks their visitors offered with surprised delight. The Jesuits scornfully reported that all Chinese timekeepers were inaccurate, even the sundials, which were made as though all the world lived at 36 degrees of latitude. (This being where they had been built.)

Besides sundials and primitive water clocks, the main timepieces seem to have been candle or incense clocks which sometimes had different aromas placed at different levels so people could actually smell the time. Su Sung's marvellous clock had been carried off by invaders and broken into pieces, and so was remembered only in dusty manuscripts. It was not until this century, when written accounts of it were rediscovered, that it was restored to its rightful place in the history of time.

EGG ON THEIR FACES Water clocks were popular in Europe but, with winters consistently harder than they are today,

John Combridge, an American Post Office engineer and amateur horologist, built models to show the probable workings of Su Sung's mechanical water clock, (right), only discovered by science historians in the 1950s. He learnt Chinese specially so he could read original descriptions of the mechanism. Housed in an elaborate astronomical tower, the clock's driving force was a giant wooden wheel with a series of scoops linked to balance levers. As the scoops filled with water, the wheel moved round, one spoke at a time. It also had a striking mechanism, to signal hours, quarters, and night watches.

they were of limited use. Sand- or hourglasses appeared from the fourteenth century onwards although, strictly speaking, they should not have been called sandglasses at all. Their 'sand' was actually powdered eggshell – true sand was too thick.

Early mechanical clocks were expensive and cumbersome, they wore out quickly and, worst of all, they were less than accurate. Mistrust of these new-fangled mechanisms led many people to use old ways of timekeeping as well.

A case in point is the elaborate turret clock constructed in Perpignan in France in 1356. The cost, according to one modern writer, must have been the equivalent of well over half a million dollars. A workforce of nearly one hundred people laboured on this device, which was the wonder of its age. When the huge bell was successfully cast, the royal family and entire workforce celebrated with a feast.

However, after a few years the clock began to give endless trouble. When it was just over 30 years old, the king decided to give it a helping hand. He hired two men at a penny a day to ring the hours, tracking the time with a sandglass.

The old ways, apparently, were not only better – they were cheaper.

FRÈRE JACQUES   The English word 'clock' is linked to the French word *cloche*, meaning 'bell', and the word gives a clue to the clock's early origins.

'Frère Jacques', that popular childhood nursery rhyme, is a reminder that some of the most fanatical timekeepers in the Middle Ages were monks. ('Brother John, Are you sleeping? Ring the bell for Matins… Ding, ding, dong.') The monastic day was punctuated by services that had to be

The oldest surviving working clock in the world is at Salisbury Cathedral. It has no dials or hands but it does strike the hours. It was built in 1386 – 30 years after the unfortunate clock at Perpignan, of which no trace remains. It was restored in 1956, having struck the hours for 498 years and ticked more than 500 million times. At the Science Museum in London, the mechanism of the Wells Cathedral clock, also dating from the late fourteenth century, is preserved. With three sets of wheels for going, striking, and quarter chiming, it has gearing for an astronomical dial. The movement was in use at Wells until 1835.

performed exactly on time, so monasteries provided a ready market for timepieces that worked.

Long after mechanical clocks first arrived on the scene, which was somewhere around the fourteenth century, they remained primarily the preserve of monasteries and churches. There is a story of a duel at Hainault in Essex, which was meant to be held at dawn. Only one duellist turned up and, after he had twiddled his pistols for the prescribed waiting period, he asked for the non-appearance of his rival to be legally recorded. The problem was that no one was sure of the exact time – nine o'clock being the agreed deadline – so someone had to be despatched to the nearest church to find out.

Public clocks, usually found in town squares and marketplaces, eventually joined the religious ones. They struck the hours, not just the times of religious observances, and soon served an important role in cities. But private clocks were a different matter. The diarist, Samuel Pepys (1633-7103) – who was probably not untypical of mid-seventeenth-century man – had no clock or watch, but used the sundials and clocks of London.

THE SAD CASE OF SIR CLOUDESLEY SHOVELL Admiral Sir Cloudesley Shovell (1650-1707) was a force to be reckoned with in the British Navy during the days of piracy on the high seas. He put a torch to four men-of-war belonging to Tripolitan pirates and saw service in Bantry Bay, Beachy Head, Gibraltar and Malaga. And, as the seventeenth century turned into the eighteenth, he was made Commander-in-Chief of the British Fleet.

Unfortunately, his glorious naval career came to an abrupt end one squally night in September 1707, when he

and over 2000 sailors were shipwrecked and drowned off the Scilly Isles. The cause was hopelessly incompetent navigation.

The Admiral had been returning home at the head of the fleet from an abortive attack on Toulon. It was foggy, and no one was too sure where they were. The majority opinion seemed to be that they were off the coast of France. One dissenting voice, according to legend, was that of a sailor on the Admiral's ship, the *Association*. He is said to have been hanged from the yardarm for his insolence in suggesting that they were actually off the Scilly Isles.

In thick fog and gales, the *Association* splintered into matchwood on the Gilstone Ledges, and all its 900-strong crew drowned. The *Eagle* and *Romney*, which had been following, also struck rocks. Of all the sailors on board, only one survived.

The body of Admiral Sir Cloudesley Shovell, along with that of his pet Italian greyhound, was washed up on the shores of St Mary's Island the next day. Scillonians were never slow to take advantage of the unfortunate victims of their rocks and, by the time the Admiral's body was officially discovered, it had been stripped of its shirt and two rings. Years later, a woman on her deathbed is said to have confessed that the Admiral was still alive when he was washed up, but she had murdered him for his finery.

Sceptics on the island said that the sailors were drunk, and that was why their ships had hit the rocks, but the official view was that the prime cause was inadequate navigational instruments. Finding a ship's latitude was relatively easy, using an astrolabe to measure the altitude of the sun at noon, but finding the longitude remained little better than a guess and a prayer. On 8 July 1714, seven years after

When Admiral Sir Cloudesley Shovell (left) died in a shipwreck off the Scilly Isles it led to a public outcry over the inefficiency of navigational instruments. His men had thought they were off the coast of France – in fact, they were close to some of the most hazardous rocks in the British Isles.

the wreck of the *Association*, Queen Anne gave the Royal Assent to 'A Bill for Providing a Public Reward for Such Person or Persons as Shall Discover the Longitude at Sea'. Enter, stage right, an unknown Yorkshire carpenter called John Harrison.

'LONGITUDE' HARRISON The puzzle of longitude had exercised many of the best minds in the country for years. A mere royal prize was not going to solve it overnight, but it certainly acted as an incentive. In the madhouse scene from *A Rake's Progress*, published in 1735, Hogarth included a man trying to calculate longitude. He had a point – some of the solutions that had been offered in the past bordered on the lunatic.

Take the case of Digby's dog. Sir Kenelm Digby was a dilettante gentleman who had invented a supposedly miraculous healing powder that was said to work by indirect application to a wound. He claimed to have made his patients jump merely by dipping their dressings into his 'powder of sympathy'. Some bright spark came up with the idea of carrying a wounded dog on a ship and, meanwhile back at home, dipping some powdered bandages from the dog's wound into a bowl of water every hour. The dog would obligingly yelp, and the frequency of his yelps could be compared to local time. What happened when the dog's wound was cured does not seem to have been considered but, at any rate, the idea was soon discounted.

On land, longitude could be calculated by plotting the position of the moon in relation to certain planets, but

John Harrison (1693–1776) was the Yorkshire carpenter and self-taught clock-maker who beat some of the highest experts in the land with his invention of the marine chronometer. The device revolutionised navigation and saved countless lives.

this involved calculations too complicated for the average sailor. Most seamen relied on dead reckoning, which meant keeping careful records of compass courses and speed. However, the only way they knew of estimating speed was by throwing a line overboard and then timing how far the ship travelled along a measured length. The measurements were recorded in the ship's log, so-called because the line was usually weighted with a piece of log.

The idea of using a clock to measure longitude, by comparing the time at sea with the time back home, was first canvassed way back in the sixteenth century. Sadly, there

Longitude and lunacy ... the man behind the door in this mad-house scene by Hogarth is trying to calculate longitude.

was one fundamental problem – there were no accurate clocks. Ironically enough, the first ship to carry an experimental clock for longitude measurement at sea itself fell victim to the problems of navigation.

In April 1741, the *Centurion* rounded Cape Horn, but adverse currents prevented it from travelling as far west as planned. Since many of his men were dying from scurvy, the ship's captain was keen to land on the island of Juan Fernandez for fresh supplies of food and water. However, uncertainty over the exact location of both the island, and his own ship, meant that he did not get there until the middle of June. Meanwhile, nearly 70 men had died.

The clock, which the *Centurion* had tested out five years before this mishap, had a special kind of balance

Harrison's Number 1 (left), along with numbers 2 (above), 3 (page 87) and 4 (page 88), are housed in a special room in the National Maritime Museum in Greenwich. Later marine chronometers used different mechanisms, based on French models, but Harrison was the first to prove that longitude could be measured with a special clock.

JOHN HARRISON

spring. Pendulum clocks had long since been ruled out because they were too strongly affected by the movement of the ship. But the balance spring turned out to be not much better, as it ran slow in high temperatures and fast in cold ones.

It was left to a landlubber and self-taught clockmaker, John Harrison, to come up with the first working marine chronometer. Born at Foulby in Yorkshire, Harrison was the eldest son of a poor carpenter. The story goes that he first became interested in clockmaking at the age of six. He was recovering from an attack of smallpox and his parents put a watch on his pillow to amuse him. Unwittingly, they set the pattern for his life.

He was just 21 years old when Parliament announced the prize of £20 000 which would be awarded to the person who could find a suitably accurate method of determining longitude. Twenty thousand pounds were untold riches to someone like Harrison – worth well over a million pounds in today's money – and it was a challenge he could not refuse.

Harrison had already taught himself to make and repair clocks, and this profitable sideline was overtaking his original trade as a carpenter. He also studied mechanics and physics, but he was a perfectionist, and not one to rush into things.

His first clocks were made mainly of wood, which was cheaper than brass, and used all his skills as a carpenter. With the help of his brother, James, he concentrated on making them as accurate as possible before turning his attention to the project in hand. It was not until 1730, when he was 37 years old, that he first went up to London with his ideas for a clock to be used at sea. And it was not until five years after that that his sketches and models were turned into a working mechanism.

H 1, as his first chronometer was later called, was a large and cumbersome clock. Even so, the Royal Society scientists who looked at it thought it showed promise, with its system of interconnected balances to counteract the rolling of the ship. They put it to a sea trial on the *Centurion* and were impressed.

However, the trial had only been on a voyage to Lisbon, and the rules of the competition specified a trip to the West Indies. The prizewinning device was to be accurate to within 30 miles (48 kilometres). In the case of a clock, this meant that, after six weeks at sea, it would have to be accurate to within two minutes.

Harrison's H 2 was never tested because it was finished in time of war and there were fears it might fall into enemy hands. For the next 19 years he beavered away at his next version, H 3. This had an advanced mechanism which foreshadowed modern ball-bearings, but, before even offering this for trial, he had started work on a fourth chronometer.

H 4 was more like a large watch, but on this Harrison finally rested his hopes. 'I think I may make bold to say,' he wrote, 'that there is neither any other Mechanism or

Mathematical thing in the World that is more beautiful or curious in texture than this my watch or Time-keeper for the Longitude.'

It represented a lifetime's work and, by the time it came up for trial, Harrison was too old to make the trip himself. Instead, William acompanied the chronometer on its journey to Jamaica. It proved itself magnificently, falling well within the permissible limits of error. However, the imposingly-named Board of Longitude were reluctant to award the prize. They gave Harrison a paltry £2500 and told him they needed further proof that his chronometer worked.

The truth was that many influential members of the scientific establishment still pinned their hopes on an alternative method of finding longitude, using tables of the moon's position. And, perhaps more importantly, sheer snobbery prevented them admitting that a humble working man had beaten them to the finishing post.

Harrison's chronometer was sent to sea yet again – to Barbados this time – and did even better. Calculations showed that, on the round trip, it had been out by less than a tenth of a second a day. Still the Board of Longitude held back, demanding that Harrison should divulge all his secrets and, even more incredible, build yet another timepiece.

By now an old man, Harrison had had enough. He enlisted the help of no less a person than George III. The King took a personal interest in tests on the performance of chronometer number five and, impressed by the results, told Harrison to petition Parliament. Parliament, knowing Harrison had the King's backing, finally awarded him the money.

In 1773, Harrison eventually received his reward. An exact replica of his fourth chronometer was at the same time voyaging round Australia and New Zealand with Captain Cook. But recognition of its creator had come only just in time. Harrison died in 1776, satisfied with the completion of his task but embittered by his treatment from the men in London. As he wrote to the Board of Longitude, 'I hope I am the first, and for my country's sake, shall be the last that suffers from pinning my faith on an English Act of Parliament.'

TIME PRESENT AND TIME PAST In 1992, holders of Barclays Bank gold charge-cards were offered the chance to celebrate the coming New Year in both Ireland and Bermuda, thanks to the time-travelling potential of Concorde. Leaving Shannon Airport just after midnight, they were scheduled to arrive in Bermuda a full hour before they left – just in time to crack open a second bottle of champagne.

Some people feel that the romance of travel has died with the arrival of the jet age. Transported in an air-conditioned tin can from one antiseptic waiting lounge to another, there is no real sense of going places. In any case, if you can buy Scots shortbread in a tartan tin in the Duty Free shop, why bother going to the real place? It's usually raining, anyway.

Be that as it may, aeroplanes have certainly confused our sense of time. Whole chunks of the day can appear and disappear at the press of a digital watch button as you travel through another time zone. And, if you cross the International Date Line, which runs down the Pacific Ocean, you can gain or lose a whole day.

Before the introduction of time zones – when travel was slower, anyway – time change was a gentler business,

Flying at speeds of well over 1000 miles (1600 km) an hour, Concorde has made time travel an everyday possibility. In the old days, when circling the world in 80 days was a major achievement, adjustments in time were made gradually. But jet travel and international time zones have changed all that.

with 1 minute allowed for every 14 miles (22 kilometres) in the UK. But this meant that, even in a small country like Britain, virtually every other civic clock was set to a different time. To the west of the Greenwich meridian, local time was earlier, and to the east it was later.

Stage-coach drivers got round the problem by using special watches which were set to run fast or slow depending on the direction in which they were travelling. But by the middle of the nineteenth century, the coming of the railways had led to the imposition of so-called 'railway time'. This was based on Greenwich

Mean Time, and was distributed around the country by electric signals transmitted by wires running alongside railway tracks. The many timetables listed in the famous *Bradshaw's Railway Guide* (first published in 1832) would have been a nonsense without a uniform time system.

Rural areas, though, still kept fondly to the old ways of timekeeping, and this led to the famous court case of Curtis v March, held at Dorchester Assizes in 1858. The case was a dispute over some land and was set to be heard at 10 a.m. The judge donned his wig at what he took to be the right time and, when neither the defendant nor his lawyer appeared, found against them. Two minutes after his decision, the defendant turned up – late by the court clock, but on time by local clocks.

Incidents such as this, and similar problems over what time to close election ballot boxes, led to an Act of Parliament in 1880 making Greenwich Mean Time the legal time for all purposes throughout the UK.

BEING 'BENNED' Big Ben, in St Stephen's Tower in the Houses of Parliament in London, was the biggest and most accurate clock of the nineteenth century. Although it no longer gets full marks for accuracy, it still has a firm place in the national psyche.

Its chimes – with music taken from Handel's *Messiah* – are recorded live each day for the six o'clock and midnight news on BBC Radio Four. Yet although the striking of the hour is reliable, the chimes are not. They can start at anywhere between 25 and 18 seconds before the hour and, if they are late, the newsreader may find his or her voice being drowned by the chimes of the hour. It is known in the trade as being 'benned'.

First set in motion on 31 May 1859, Big Ben was originally wound by hand three times a week. (Winding is now done electronically.) There are 350 steps inside St Stephen's Tower, the first hundred of them beside bricked-up windows – a reminder of the time when they belonged to the prison cells of Westminster. The four dials of Big Ben were designed by that master of the Gothic Revival, Augustus Welby Pugin (1812-52), and cost more than the clock mechanism and bells combined.

Big Ben's 13-foot (3.9-metre) long pendulum is made of zinc and iron, to withstand changes in temperature. Variations in barometric pressure, however, can still affect its timing, so pennies are used to keep it accurate. Add a penny, and the clock gains about $^4/_{10}$ of a second in 24 hours. Take one away, and it loses by the same amount. Old pennies are used, rather than new, because they weigh exactly 1 oz (28 g).

The bells of Big Ben were silenced during the First World War, much to the distress of Londoners, in case they helped German airships find their way around the city. During the Second World War, the House of Commons was bombed on 14 occasions, but Big Ben still kept perfect time, even when flames were leaping up the clock tower. It took a flock of starlings to achieve what Hitler had failed to do. In 1945, they sat on the minute hand – and slowed it down by five minutes.

Big Ben flew apart early one August morning in 1976, and hundreds

The clock tower at the Houses of Parliament, in London, is known to the world as Big Ben. The name Big Ben was originally applied only to the great bell, cast in 1858, and weighing over 13 tons, but it is now used to describe the whole tower. No one knows for certain how Big Ben got its name. It could have been a reference to the girth of Sir Benjamin Hall, the Victorian MP and Commissioner of Works whose name is inscribed on the side of the bell. Or it could have come from the pugilist, Benjamin Count (nickname Big Ben) who was fighting in London when the bell was being tested in New Palace Yard.

of people wrote in offering to help repair it. Eventually, with the aid of radiographical testing of new and renovated parts, it was restored just in time for the Queen's Jubilee in 1977. Only one important person was not there to hear its rejuvenated bells. John Darwin, the resident engineer, had had a heart attack while running up the many steps of the clock tower. He spent Jubilee Day recovering in hospital.

The Fortnum and Mason clock, installed above the gourmet emporium in Piccadilly in 1964, incorporates effigies of the firm's founders. At every chime, the pair appear, bow to each other and retire. Mr Fortnum – once a footman at Buckingham Palace – is dressed in footman's livery. Mr Mason wears the traditional dress of an eighteenth-century grocer. The clock, built at a cost of £25 000, was made by Thwaites and Reed, clock-makers by Royal Appointment. Originally based in Clerkenwell in London and now operating from modern workshops in Hastings in Sussex, Thwaites and Reed claim to be the oldest firm of clock-makers in Britain. Their first clock, made for the Horse Guards Parade in 1740, is still in use. They were also involved in the rebuilding of Big Ben's quarter chime works in 1977.

'TIME RULES EVERYTHING' The very fact that the Victorians saw fit to give such prominence to a clock on their new House of Commons says something about the age in which they lived. As the motto on Big Ben states, 'Time rules everything'.

In its early days, Parliament had been more like a leisurely gentleman's club. Late sittings were rare – so much so that, when members sat by candlelight to pass the Petition of Rights in 1621, James I tore it up. It had, he said, been 'passed at an unreasonable hour'.

With the expansion of the British Empire, and the arrival of greater responsibilities, the House of Commons sat for longer and longer sessions. Clocks were used in an attempt to keep members to the point – not always successfully. The British House of Commons now sits for longer than any other parliament in the world.

Knowing what the time is does not necessarily mean you will use it efficiently. Time and motion experts have found that, in an average 40-hour working week, only about 8 hours are actually spent in productive work. A Gallup Poll, carried out for British Telecom, among Britain's 700 000 secretaries found that they spent two-thirds of their working week on routine mechanics. Top of the list was telephoning, which accounted for the equivalent of two full days a week. Then came faxing and photocopying (half a day each), sorting the post and filing.

Endless surveys have trumpeted the time and motion benefits of working from home, yet the latest forecasts suggest that, by 1995, only 1.3 million people in Britain will be doing so. It could be partly because people are so sociable, but it could also be because they like a bit of built-in inefficiency.

Tennis players may think they are paid to play tennis but they will probably spend less than a fifth of a match hitting the ball. Ivan Lendl and Michael Chang spent 3 hours 20 minutes on court at Munich. Yet when the match was over, someone calculated that the ball had only actually been in play for 38 minutes. The rest of the time had been spent waiting for a ball, drinking squash or preparing to serve. No doubt that is why promoters are so keen to use tennis players as walking sandwich boards.

In the mid-Victorian age, industrialisation in Britain ate away into people's leisure time. Sundays always remained sacrosanct, but the granting of Saturday afternoons as holidays only came as a result of pressure from unions, and concessions from managements. The word 'weekend' wasn't coined until the late nineteenth century and, even then, the idea of having two consecutive days off did not really come of age until well into this century. Until the end of the First World War, there were no limits on the working week: people of all ages worked very long hours. It was not until the 1920s that research started into the benefits of tea breaks and so on. The idea that people could actually work better after a break was anathema to most employers.

A FRIDAY CAR The day most people are absent from work is Fridays, followed closely by Monday. In the 1960s, the problem was so bad that some car manufacturers had to cancel their late shift on a Friday simply because the workers weren't turning up to do it. Hence the term 'a Friday car', meaning a dud because no one was around to build it properly. According to one study, the UK has the worst record of absenteeism in the industrialised world, with 113 million working hours lost each year.

Some people have phobias about particular days of the week, or particular dates (like Friday the 13th). Others, according to a Californian physician, may suffer from a more general time sickness. Dr Larry Dossey likens time sickness to claustrophobia – the fear of enclosed spaces. Time-sick people feel hemmed in by the passage of time, and the resulting panic attacks render them incapable of achieving anything.

Clocks and watches have always been regarded as a

How secretaries really spend their time …

Telephone:	16 hr 25 min
Faxing:	3 hr 50 min
Copying:	3 hr 15 min
Sorting Post:	
	2 hr 35 min
Filing:	1 hr 40 min

Source: Gallup Poll for British Telecom, November 1991.

mixed blessing. When the eighteenth-century philosopher Jean Jacques Rousseau decided he wanted to reject civilisation and return to a state of nature, his watch was the first thing to go. Samuel Butler, in his satirical book *Erewhon* (published in 1872), went one stage further. In his Utopian land divested of all machinery, the simple possession of a watch was an imprisonable offence.

FROM WATCHES TO EXPLODING CLOCKS   One of the earliest historical mentions of a watch was when Henry VIII gave one to his fifth wife, Catherine Howard. (Perhaps to remind her that her time was limited.)

Country people, though, regarded early watches with deep suspicion. The story goes that the sixteenth-century Oxford don, Thomas Allen, once left his watch in his room while the maids came in to make the bed. Hearing it tick, they thought it was the don's personal devil and hurled it out of the window. The fact that it caught in the branches of a tree only confirmed its devilish credentials.

Timing on the battlefield being all-important, soldiers used to take their roosters with them so they could be sure of waking at daybreak. By the eighteenth century, though, roosters were being replaced by watches. Watch-makers based in the Swiss mountains found a ready market as they tailed the French imperial army all over Europe while selling them their wares.

The Swiss made a speciality of musical and moving watches of all descriptions. Automaton watches showed little moving figures, such as Moses striking the rock to bring forth water, that struck the hours and quarters. By the early nineteenth century erotic watches were popular, with lewd scenes hidden behind a small flap. These often depicted

clergymen in unlikely positions – a sign of the widespread anticlericalism of the time.

Clocks were similary inventive – particularly the large public clocks that became fashionable in the nineteenth century. The central attraction at the Bull Ring Market in Birmingham was once a giant metal and wood automated clock, built in 1883. Known affectionately as Percy's clock, after the alderman responsible for its restoration in the 1930s, it had 7-foot (2-metre) high carvings of a medieval Saracen and a Crusader. Every hour, the Saracen and the Crusader smashed a huge white bell to sound the time.

Until the First World War, wristwatches were primarily for ladies. But fob watches are hardly practical if you are crawling through mud, so soldiers started wearing them, too. Synchronised wrist-watches sent men over the top at 7.30 a.m. on 1 July 1916 for the start of the Battle of the Somme. The British sustained 60 000 casualties – 20 000 of them fatal – in the heaviest single loss of the war. Most soldiers were mown down by machine guns within the first few minutes of the offensive. Disastrous casualties at Gallipoli were caused by a bombardment which stopped five minutes too early, leaving Allied ranks exposed to machine gun fire.

Recently, moves were set afoot to rebuild the clock, which had been destroyed by bombs in 1940, but Birmingham City Council, ever sensitive to the ethnic implications of such things, were less than keen. Even when it was pointed out to them that the Saracen and Crusader were working together to strike the bell – rather than bashing away at each other – they were not convinced.

When quartz mechanisms of unbelievable accuracy first hit the market in the 1960s, it seemed as if the days of mechanical clocks and watches were numbered, but there are still plenty of craftsmen who take a pride in the old ways. Meanwhile, a new generation of inventors has made clocks highly fashionable as architectural showpieces. The star attraction at the Eureka Children's Museum in Halifax is an Archimedes bath clock, and a focal point at the Ebbw Vale Garden Festival in Wales was a 29-foot (9-metre) high exploding clock, designed to add a bit of a spice to a drab shopping precinct in Newport. Made of stainless steel, it looks like a giant classical portico – but on the hour a door opens in one of the columns and a devil appears. Two skeletons pop out of other compartments, shaking hourglasses before retreating. Then the huge structure dramatically splits open, accompanied by thunder, smoke and flashing lights. The clock itself is really electronic but, when it opens, it reveals fake weights and a cuckoo. Hence its nickname, 'the thundering cuckoo'.

THE TIMES THEY ARE A-CHANGING The average British household has at least 10 timepieces, if you take into account watches, clocks, central heating timers, video recorders and ovens. That's fine when they are all working away happily, but what about when we have to adjust them for British Summer Time?

One watch-making company has estimated that a total of 1 750 000 man hours are spent putting the clocks forward in the spring, and another 1 750 000 are used putting them back again in the autumn. Put another way, that's almost 400 years spent adjusting clocks each year. Assuming, of course, you remember to change the clocks at all. An estimated three million people in Britain forget each time, despite warnings in newspapers, on radio and on television.

To avoid such problems, one British company has invented an 'intelligent' digital alarm clock, which keeps near-perfect time by tuning into the National Physical Laboratory's radio time signal broadcast from Rugby. The clock's alarm plays a digital recording of Fenella Fielding's voice which becomes more insistent the longer you snooze on – and it resets itself each time the clocks go forward or backwards. A German company introduced a wristwatch based on a similar system at the end of 1990.

Many countries in the world operate some form of daylight saving time (Britain's was introduced in 1916) to make the most of the daylight during the summer months, but a growing number of people in Britain think that, for political as well as practical reasons, we should abandon British Summer Time. The Daylight Extra Action Group was set up in 1989 to lobby for the adoption of Central European Time – Greenwich Mean Time plus one hour in winter, and plus two in summer. Members include British Rail and Eurotunnel, who are alarmed at the logistical problems of sending trains through a tunnel from one time zone to another. Safety experts also favour the change, saying it is a way of preventing accidents on dark winter evenings.

Water clock at Neal's Yard in Covent Garden, London, designed by inventor Tim Hunkin, one of a new generation of clock enthusiasts. His Archimedes Clock at the Eureka Children's Museum in Halifax uses a standard factory clock to trigger a dramatic half hourly display. Not only does the copper figure of Archimedes plop in and out of his bath, but the water he displaces is sucked back up by a giant Archimedean screw. All very educational – but also great fun.

This assemblage of shining metal may not look like a clock, but it ticks over nine billion times a second. The caesium clock at the National Physical Laboratory in Teddington supplies the time for British Telecom's Timeline, and also helps to keep Big Ben on time. It works by using electrical impulses to make atoms of caesium vibrate, sending out electromagnetic waves of very precise frequency.

Yet Britain is by no means the only country to have problems with its clocks. The Russians faced major confusion in January 1992 when they suddenly had to lose an hour overnight – all because of a mistake made by Stalin over 60 years earlier. The dictator instituted summer time in the spring of 1930, calling it 'decree time', but apparently forgot to turn the clocks back in the autumn. As much to save electricity as to give its people more daylight, the government belatedly decided to put things right.

China has one single time zone, stretching about 3000 miles (4830 kilometres) from Shanghai to Tibet. Scientists at key observatories tune in to Soviet Television every evening in order to check their atomic clocks. By timing the television signal's arrival, they can tell if their clocks are running fast or slow.

WORLD-BEATING CLOCKS In 1992 the Hewlett-Packard company of California, suppliers of timepieces to the military, unveiled the latest in clock-making precision. It is an atomic clock, the size of a desktop computer, which is accurate to 1 second in 1.6 million years.

Since the 1940s, scientists have known that the electrons of atoms oscillate with a rhythm so regular that, like a pendulum, they could be used to tell the time. Atomic clocks use atoms of caesium, a silver white metal, and are accurate not just to a microsecond, but to a nanosecond (a billionth of a second). Clocks are now better timekeepers than the earth itself for, like an unwinding clock, the world is gradually spinning more and more slowly. Since 1972, scientists have compensated for this, by adding a leap-second to most years.

The earth's speed of rotation depends on several factors, including wind speeds, ocean movements and activity deep in the planet's core. The Paris-based International Earth Rotation Service keeps tabs on the globe, and tells scientists when the leap-second correction should be made.

Such an obsession with accuracy may seem ridiculous; but without the leap-second, those lost seconds would add up. For ships navigating at sea, for instance, a one-second mistake could make a difference of $1/4$ mile (0.4 kilometre). Satellite navigation systems, astronomers, military and computer experts all rely on super-accurate timing.

Whether the world will still be here in 1.6 million years' time, so Hewlett-Packard's claims for its atomic clock can be checked, is a moot point. But maybe, if it is, such mind-boggling accuracy will by then seem as primitive as the sundial is to us.

THE CRYPT OF CIVILISATION Deep in a granite basement of Oglethorpe University in Atlanta, Georgia, lies the Crypt of Civilisation – the most ambitious time capsule ever made. Sealed up in 1940, a 20-foot (6-metre) long room contains a sample of everything its creators considered necessary for the re-creation of civilised life. It includes microfilm of over 800 written works, from the Bible to *Gone with the Wind*, Donald Duck toys and paper clips, an ampoule of Budweiser beer, a set of spark plugs and even a potato masher.

No one knows for sure, of course, what state civilisation will be in by the time the great door is broken down. So, just in case, there is a hand-operated teach-yourself-English machine at the entrance. Time capsule enthusiasts who went to the fiftieth anniversary celebrations in May 1990 were given brass plaques inviting any of their descendants to the ceremonial opening of the crypt – at noon in the year 8113.

In 1957, the residents of Tulsa, Oklahoma, buried a Plymouth car. People were invited to guess what the population of Tulsa would be in 2057, when the car will be dug up. It will then be offered as a prize to the family of the person whose guess was nearest the mark. The car will come complete, of course, with a tank full of petrol at twenty-first-century prices.

Time capsules are nothing new. When Cleopatra's Needle was placed on the Embankment in London, in 1878, a sealed box was built into its pedestal. It included a complete set of Victorian money, as well as a 2-foot rule and a standard pound weight. There were also copies of

Atomic clocks have enabled astronomers to measure the distance from the earth to the moon to the nearest $3/4$ inch (1.9 cm). Their secret is the set of reflectors set up on the moon's Sea of Tranquillity by the American astronauts Neil Armstrong and Edwin 'Buzz' Aldrin. German astronomers working at the Carl Zeiss company in Germany calculated the distance using a powerful laser telescope. They shone a laser beam on the reflectors and, using an atomic clock, measured the time it took for the signal to travel to the moon and back.

Whitaker's Almanack and *Bradshaw's Railway Guide*, a portrait of Queen Victoria, a shilling razor and a box of cigars. Working presumably on the assumption that anyone who was heathen enough to crack open the pedestal of Cleopatra's Needle might also be heathen in their religion, there were also copies of the Bible, plus a translation into 215 different languages of Chapter 3, Verse 16 of St John's Gospel ('God so loved the world, that he gave his only begotten son. . .').

The term 'time capsule' was coined by the PR department of the American company, Westinghouse, who buried an 880-lb (399-kg) copper alloy cylinder under Flushing Meadow at the New York World's Fair in 1938. Stainless steel time capsules are now manufactured commercially in the United States, and have also become popular in other industrialised countries.

Dr Brian Durrans, an anthropologist at the Museum of Mankind in London and founder member of the

International Time Capsule Society, thinks such capsules may well prove to be totally bewildering to future generations. Whoever digs up the Westinghouse capsule, for instance, will get a highly distorted view of the world importance of a company called Westinghouse Electric and Manufacturing. And since such capsules are, by definition, self-conscious productions, they are unlikely to reflect life as it was really lived at that time. 'The idea of wanting to be remembered is something we all have,' said Dr Durrans, 'but it's only the serious time encapsulators who take it to such lengths.'

He has gathered information on well over 300 capsules, most of them in the United States and Britain. 'People don't see the need to blow trumpets about them,' he said. 'The majority are very individual or family activities. They're anecdotal, they're jokey, they're done with a nervous laugh. When they attempt to anticipate what the future might be like, they usually fall flat on their face.' Dr Durrans sees the prime motivation as being an attempt to impose order on an uncertain future, an investment in posterity.

Craftsmen have always made 'signature' marks on their work, as a silent message for future generations. A modern equivalent seems to be the man from British Aerospace who intermittently wrote out chunks of poetry and slotted them between the layers of laminated fuselage. He chose such poets as John Donne, and William Shakespeare, and even the notoriously bad verse of Scots poet William McGonagall was preserved in this way.

True time capsules can be seen as signs either of great optimism or of great pessimism. 'The assumption may be that the future is going to be onwards and upwards, in which case the present would be seen as rather quaint,' said

Dr Durrans. 'But the alternative is that civilisation might take a nose-dive. People are very aware of the fact that great civilisations of the past don't seem to have passed seamlessly from one to the next. So in that sense, what's being attempted is a kind of blueprint that could almost give a collapsed civilisation the opportunity to rebuild.'

Meanwhile, he is still trying to track down one of the great lost time capsules of the century – a container with 22 million American signatures, stolen from the Bicentennial Wagon Train in 1976. When President Ford arrived for the sealing ceremony at Valley Forge, Pennsylvania, the capsule was nowhere to be found.

If it ever turns up, its inscrutable hieroglyphics will no doubt provide one more puzzle for future historians.

Prisoners of war forced to slave on Japan's 'Death Railway' in the Thai jungle during World War Two. Some of those who survived returned in February 1992 to bury a time capsule in a stretch known as 'Hellfire Pass,' where it is said that one prisoner died for every railway sleeper laid. Altogether, some 13 000 Allied prisoners of war and 80 000 labourers, most of them Thais, Burmese and Malays, died of starvation or disease. The capsule is intended to be opened in 2042 – a century after work on the railway started.

TEMPERATURE

SCIENTISTS HAVE NOW discovered hitherto undreamed-of extremes of temperature, both hot and cold. At the JET (Joint European Torus) nuclear fusion project in Culham, Oxfordshire, researchers have reached temperatures of up to 200 million °C (392 million °F) – many times hotter than the centre of the sun. At the Low Temperature Laboratory in Helsinki, Finland, a team of physicists has created what may be the coldest spot in the universe by cooling helium to only two billionths of a degree above absolute zero. This is cold beyond an Eskimo's worst nightmares – colder even than the frozen wastes of outer space.

Finding accurate ways of measuring temperature may have been a small step for man, but it was a giant leap for mankind. From test tube babies to the chilling art of cryonics, many scientific advances would simply have been impossible without the invention of the thermometer.

Thermoscopes, the ancestors of thermometers, have been around since at least 200 BC. The physicist and philosopher, Philo of Byzantium, described an experiment to show the expansion of air with heat. He took two containers – one filled with water, the other containing only air –

The JET project, funded and staffed by 14 European countries, aims to prove that it is possible to obtain cheap, plentiful and clean energy from nuclear fusion – the same heat-intensive process that fuels the stars and the hydrogen bomb.

and linked them with a tube. Placed in the sun, air flowed into the water, producing bubbles. In the shade, water rose up the tube into the air-filled vessel.

Science historians differ on who should be given the credit for inventing the first modern thermometer. Two prime candidates seem to be the Italian physicist Galileo Galilei (1564-1642), and Santorio Santorio (1561-1636), one-time physician to the King of Poland, and Professor of Medicine at the University of Padua. (He was the man, you may remember, who spent the best part of 30 years of his life sitting in a home-made weighing machine.)

Both men were undoubtedly working on thermoscopes at about the same time, but Santorio provided the first written account (in 1612) of an instrument using a scale. His later writings also suggested that he understood the value of the thermometer in diagnosing disease.

The first sealed thermometer was invented by Grand Duke Ferdinand of Tuscany in 1641. He took the device as used by Galileo and Santorio, turned it upside down, and sealed up the end. As well as the obvious practical advantages of this move, it meant that his thermometers were more accurate, as they were not affected by changes in atmospheric pressure.

In 1657, he founded the Accademia del Cimento in Florence where, until it was disbanded 10 years later, his team of scientists developed thermometers filled with both alcohol and mercury. He had the services of some of the best glass-blowers in Europe, and his instruments were true works of art.

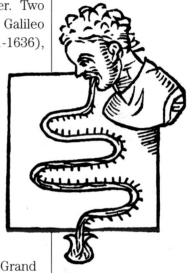

Santorio's clinical thermometers were designed either to be hand-held, or put in the mouth. All had a bulb at the top and a tube dipping into an open fluid-filled vessel.

Lancaster University professors George Pickett and Tony Guénault stand beside their home-made helium fridge, a Heath Robinson-style assembly of beer barrels and pipes that lead to a sealed tin-plated room. The slightest disturbance could generate heat, and a sign at the entrance of the room reads 'If door shut, ask permission for entry. Signed: St Peter.' Using this equipment, the professors have reached temperatures as low as 12 millionths of a degree above absolute zero. The world record, held by the Low Temperature Laboratory in Helsinki, is two billionths. Even the coldest spot in outer space is a comparatively warm 2.7° above absolute zero.

FAHRENHEIT, CELSIUS AND THE IDEA OF SCALE

In the early days, there were almost as many temperature scales as there were thermometer-makers. One man's idea of extreme hot and extreme cold was unlikely to be the same as another's, so the only faintly accurate way of making comparisons was to use the same instrument several times over. Two scales which have stood the test of time, however, are those associated with the names of Gabriel Daniel Fahrenheit and Anders Celsius.

Fahrenheit was born into a prosperous merchant family in Danzig (now Gdansk), in 1686. According to some sources, he had originally been destined to study medicine, but his parents died tragically of mushroom poisoning when he was only 15, leaving him in the care of guardians. Apprenticed to a Dutch merchant house, he soon decided the commercial life was not for him. He ran away, and spent most of his early twenties wandering around Europe. It was not aimless wandering, however, for it brought him into contact with several notable scholars of the day. Among them was the Danish astronomer, Olaf Romer, whose thermometers inspired Farenheit to try to produce his own.

Fahrenheit's scale – derived from Romer's – was based on high and low points that other people could reproduce and check. His zero point was produced with a freezing mixture made from ice and salt. The melting point of ice was set at 32°, and normal body temperature at 96°. It is a tribute to Fahrenheit's skill that the presently accepted value for the body temperature of a healthy person (98.6°F) is so near to his original estimate.

The modern version of the Fahrenheit scale uses the melting point of ice and the boiling point of pure water (212°) as the lowest and highest points. It may seem a little

This is a copy of a thermometer made in about 1657 by Mariani, glass-blower to the Accademia in Florence. The base is a large alcohol-filled sphere, with a long serpentine stem in upward coils. Each coil is separated by tiny strips of glass to reduce the danger of breakage.

illogical to have a scale that starts at 32° instead of 0°, but people have simply become used to it. So much so that, despite the fact it is being officially phased out, British weather forecasters still give temperatures in Fahrenheit as well as Celsius. When they talk about 75°F it sounds like a hot day – to British ears – its Celsius equivalent (23°C) does not.

Fahrenheit's work with thermometers failed to bring him great riches. When he died, in 1736, he was given a fourth-class burial – a send-off usually reserved for the penniless. But his name lives on with his scale, which was widely adopted in British-speaking countries (although not, strangely, in his native Germany).

The Swedish astronomy professor Anders Celsius (1701-44) also has his name attached to a temperature scale. However, it is arguable that he has less reason than Fahrenheit to take the credit because his scale, as originally conceived in 1742, was upside down: it had 0° as the boiling point of water and 100° as the temperature of melting ice. It only really made sense when it was reversed, two years after his death. The two scientists – Celsius's assistant, Marten Stromer, and Christin of Lyons – who independently realised the scale should be the other way up are among the unsung heroes of temperature history.

Celsius was, however, the first

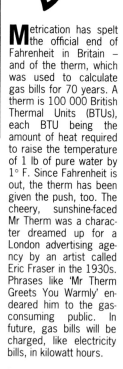

This giant thermometer on a probe was developed earlier this century to test the temperature of bread dough. The design of the head was planned so readings are clearly visible even though the scale may be poorly lit. The temperature range is from 49 to 112° F (9 – 44° C).

Metrication has spelt the official end of Fahrenheit in Britain – and of the therm, which was used to calculate gas bills for 70 years. A therm is 100 000 British Thermal Units (BTUs), each BTU being the amount of heat required to raise the temperature of 1 lb of pure water by 1° F. Since Fahrenheit is out, the therm has been given the push, too. The cheery, sunshine-faced Mr Therm was a character dreamed up for a London advertising agency by an artist called Eric Fraser in the 1930s. Phrases like 'Mr Therm Greets You Warmly' endeared him to the gas-consuming public. In future, gas bills will be charged, like electricity bills, in kilowatt hours.

to devise a Centigrade scale. He popularised mercury thermometers, and his thermometers were considerably more accurate than their predecessors.

Another important figure in the story of temperature scales is the Scottish physicist, Lord Kelvin (1824-1907). He developed the idea of absolute zero, the point of no discernible thermal energy. On the Kelvin scale, 0° K is -273.15° C.

JOSIAH WEDGWOOD AND THE PYROMETER   Conventional thermometers have several limitations – not least their tendency to explode in extreme heat. A pyrometer (literally, 'fire-measurer') is a thermometer that reaches parts no other thermometer can reach. Modern optical pyrometers enable scientists to take the temperature of lava flow on a volcano without getting their feet burnt. They can also help steel-makers test the temperature of a furnace.

One man whose work helped pave the way for the modern pyrometer was Josiah Wedgwood (1730-95), founder of the famous pottery firm. The youngest of a family of 13 children, Josiah Wedgwood was born into the pottery trade and, after serving his apprenticeship, he set up his own business in 1759.

His early speciality was everyday earthenware, but he soon became interested in the chemistry of the process he had made his life's work. He enlisted the help of such figures as Joseph Priestley, the chemist, and James Brindley, the canal engineer, in his search for new clays, glazes and enamels. One result was his famous jasper ware – pastel-coloured stoneware decorated with white classical figures.

During the course of 35 years, he carried out a series of nearly 5000 experiments, all of which were meticulously recorded in an experiment book. In Wedgwood's day, measuring the temperature inside a pottery kiln was very much a hit and miss affair. Temperatures could reach up to 1832°F (1000° C) – three times the heat existing thermometers could stand. The men operating the kilns generally used lumps of clay as a rough and ready temperature gauge, judging the temperature in the kiln by the colour of the clay inside it.

Wedgwood's first idea was a colour thermoscope, using standard samples of clay baked at different temperatures. The idea was that the firemen could compare their lumps of clay with the ready-fired ones. However, individuals see colours very differently, and the slightest discrepancy could still ruin a whole batch of pots.

At some stage in his experiments – maybe even while assembling the samples for his colour thermoscope – Wedgwood made a crucial breakthrough. Realising that clay shrinks at very high temperatures, he hit upon the idea of fitting pieces of a definite size and kind into a gauge. The higher the temperature the smaller the pieces of clay would become, and the further up the gauge they would slide. The next stage was to concoct a scale. This he did by carrying out tests at the London Mint and elsewhere to determine the melting points of brass, silver, gold and copper.

The results of his work were communicated to the Royal Society in May 1782, in a paper entitled 'An Attempt to make a Thermometer for measuring the higher Degrees of Heat, from a red Heat up to the strongest that Vessels made of clay can support.' Wedgwood always called his invention a thermometer, but we know it as the first pyrometer.

Josiah Wedgwood's pyrometer originally used pieces of pure Cornish porcelain clay, but he later had to use a mixture of clay and alumina, because he couldn't get enough natural clay. 'Wedgwood degrees' were used as the scale, with zero as the point of 'red heat', 27 as the melting point of copper and 28 that of silver. Many scientists have pointed out that Wedgwood put the melting points of silver and copper the wrong way round, but even so the general idea behind the pyrometer was influential. Pieces of clay were still used to measure the temperature of kilns until recently. The Seger cone system uses small pottery cones, each one marked with the particular temperature at which it collapses.

GETTING HOT UNDER THE COLLAR Early scientists thought that people's body temperatures varied according to where they lived, so someone living in the tropics would have a much higher natural body temperature than someone living in the Arctic Circle. We now know, of course, that that is not true. Whether you live in Timbuctoo or Tipperary, your internal thermometer will remain the same. But what about the idea of the hot-blooded Latin?

Numerous sociological studies have found that anti-social behaviour, from horn-honking to homicide, increases when it is hotter. Even in Britain, where extremes of temperature are rarer than in many other countries, crime rates rise in the summer. Burglary and theft may increase simply because people forget to lock up when the weather is warmer, but a Home Office study, published in the summer of 1992, suggested that the number of violent crimes also rose with the temperature.

Researcher Simon Field found that during months when the temperature was more than one degree above normal, crime of all kinds rose by about 2 per cent. Violence was increased by 3.4 per cent, and sexual offences by 3.6 per cent.

In practice, it may not be particularly helpful to know that the idea of a hot temper has some basis in statistics. After all, no one can turn the sun off, although air-conditioning can control the happiness and well-being of hundreds of people simply by the flick of a switch. Factory Acts set minimum temperatures for working conditions – but too much heat can be just as bad as too little, as anyone who knows that dozy

Sweaty solidarity in the steam room ... the voluptuous ladies in this painting by Ingres show clear signs of heat exhaustion. Turkish baths enjoyed widespread popularity in the nineteenth century, and many people still find them an ideal way of unwinding. Their extreme heat is supposed to rid the body of impurities and beef up the circulation.

mid-afternoon feeling in an overheated office will tell you. Experiments in factories, prisons and other institutions have found that reducing the temperature can have a dramatic effect on productivity and levels of aggression.

Some jobs, such as steel-making, involve unavoidable extremes of temperature. Twenty years ago, men would shovel manganese into molten steel by hand, wearing sweat towels round their necks. Working near temperatures of 2550–2730° F (1400-1500° C) their flat caps would disintegrate after only a few weeks. Nowadays, the process is controlled from an air-conditioned cabin.

KEEPING WARM As much as 90 per cent of our energy can be spent simply on keeping warm. The average body temperature of 98.6° F (37° C) is misleading. If you take your temperature under your armpit, it will be 1° F (0.5° C) lower than this; in the rectum, it will be 1° F (0.5° C) higher. Our bodies are cooler when we wake up and hotter when we go to sleep, and babies generally have higher body temperatures than old people.

As a general guide, the figures show that man is relatively cool-blooded. The average temperature of a stallion is 99.7° F (37.6° C) and, of a chicken, 107.1° F (41.7 °C). This would be unbearable for humans.

A hot bath might push a human's body temperature up to about 100° F (38° C), and a lengthy run could produce even hotter results. Yet this would only be measured in the rectal temperature: skin temperatures would be less than normal, due to the effect of sweating to lower the body's temperature.

Factory Acts, which set minimum temperatures for the workplace, have made thermometers such as these ones standard equipment in most factories, shops and offices.

Hippocrates thought that fever was caused by the separation of heat and cold in the body, with heat getting the upper hand. Only with the invention of the thermometer 2000 years later did our understanding of fever really advance. We now know that fever associated with illness comes when the body deliberately sets its thermostat higher (in order to kill off the infection): it does not mean the thermostat is broken.

Some people even think that humans do better when they are slightly feverish, because their metabolism is speeded up, and it is true that athletes' performances often improve towards the end of the day, when their bodies are warmer. But there is a limit to the amount of heat a body can stand.

In mild cases, overheating can cause dizziness, tiredness, fainting, swollen ankles, prickly heat and heat cramp. (Heat cramp is a painful, but not fatal, affliction common among stokers, firemen and miners.) In more severe cases, heat stroke can occur when sweating stops and body temperature soars to levels likely to produce convulsions. If the body's fluid and salts lost through sweating are not replaced, the results can be fatal.

Changes in hot and cold spots in the body can be a useful way of detecting disease. White on this picture shows the hottest parts – at 93° F (34° C) – and black represents the coolest – 78° F (26° C) or lower. Normally, the face and neck are the hottest parts of the body, and the legs and buttocks the coldest. Some physiological changes are nothing to worry about. In pregnancy, a woman's breasts are hotter than usual and her womb is colder, because it is insulated by amniotic fluid. But a deep-seated tumour, for instance, might produce an unusual patch of heat. Computerised infra-red thermography is already used to help diagnose common diseases such as arthritis. Detective work on other uses of the technique is being carried out at King's College, London – one of only three such research units in Britain.

KEEPING COLD Four-year-old Jimmy Tontlewicz confounded medical experts when he apparently came back from the dead – after 20 minutes spent underwater in a frozen lake.

Divers who plucked little Jimmy's body from the waters of Lake Michigan in the US pronounced him dead from drowning. At hospital his body temperature was found to have plummeted to below 86° F (30° C). But the doctors still tried to resuscitate him, with miraculous success. The extreme cold had apparently reduced his brain's metabolic rate, and hence its need for oxygen, and lucky Jim lived to tell the tale.

Old people can die of hypothermia when their body temperature is still a relatively warm 95° F (35° C), but small children are remarkably resilient. Two-year-old Michael Troke was found in the snow near his home in Milwaukee, Wisconsin, in January 1985, with a body temperature of 60.8° F (16° C). He survived, and earned himself a place in the *Guinness Book of Records*.

Deliberately freezing the body is a tricky business. Much medical research has been carried out in the use of frozen organs for transplantation, and in techniques of cryosurgery (using liquid nitrogen to freeze cancer cells, for example).

Then, of course, there is cryogenics. For anyone who wants to bury their body in a freezer rather than a grave, so they can be brought back to life in the future, there are immense legal and practical problems to be overcome. Not the least of them is the sheer speed at which the body decomposes once the heart stops beating. No one can plan where they die, and members of cryogenics organisations are given do-it-yourself freezing kits, just in case.

The science fiction assumption is that future genera-

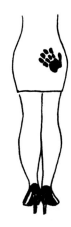

Medical thermal imaging has inspired the latest fashion gimmick – clothes that change colour with the heat. Thermochromic inks, sold under the trade name Licritherm, mean a dress can be black when it is hanging in the wardrobe and red or blue when hanging on a body. Even a stray hand print can leave a mark on it.

tions might discover the secret of eternal life or, at the very least, a cure for some terminal diseases. (Not to mention a method of revitalising all those defrosted corpses.) It is an immense leap of faith and, for the relatives of one American woman, it was a leap too far. She had left instructions that her body should be frozen after death, and so it was. But after a few years, her relatives decided to defrost her and give her a conventional burial in the earth. Eternity was clearly too long to wait.

The hedgehog in summer has a normal temperature somewhere above 92° F (33° C). When the outside temperature drops to below 57° F (14° C), the hedgehog enters its hibernation state, maintaining a steady body temperature of 43° F (6° C). Humans cannot normally hibernate, and the heart and nervous system would pack up at hedgehog body temperatures. Yet very young children have displayed an animal-like ability to survive extreme temperatures.

COOL IT! When the seventeenth-century diarist, John Evelyn, first drank Italian wine cooled with snow and ice, it gave him such a sore throat he thought he was going to die. But he recovered and, with the fervour of the newly-converted, set about preaching the ice gospel in Britain.

Ice had, in fact, been used to cool food and drink centuries before it was encountered by John Evelyn. Ice houses lined with tamarisk boughs were first recorded in ancient Mesopotamia. The Greeks used an early form of cooling box, called a psycter, for cooling wine at banquets. And both the Greeks and the Romans sold snow in vast quantities in their markets.

In Britain, ice seems to have gone the way of many other civilised comforts once the Romans left. A few monasteries had ice houses in medieval times, presumably re-importing the idea from the continent, but their use was not widespread.

By the time of the Restoration, however, ice cream and

Refrigerated trucks have some unusual uses. When the weather became too warm for the 30 penguins living at Birdland in the Cotswolds, they found a new home – in a disused ice cream lorry.

ice houses to keep it in had become the last word in luxury. Ice cream and white strawberries were served at Charles II's table for the Feast of St George at Windsor in May 1671. Lesser orders, however, had to make do with ice-less oranges and red strawberries.

Early ice houses simply used ice taken from the local pond, which was often of doubtful cleanliness. But by the mid-nineteenth-century, ice harvesting was big business. Companies such as the Knickerbocker Ice Co. of New York State sent shiploads of the stuff to every corner of the globe.

When Victorian empire-builders were posted abroad, they took their ice-keeping habits with them. Just how much they depended on the regular arrival of ice ships is shown by the ecstatic headlines which greeted the *Milton* when it arrived in Bombay in 1850: 'The MILTON! (Paradise Regained) Ice Ship has arrived.' A previous ice ship had been wrecked, and residents clearly felt cut off from civilised life as they knew it.

In the days when it was possible to roast an ox on the frozen Thames during the winter, finding a ready supply of ice was no problem in Britain. In the seventeenth century, the Thames froze over on eight recorded occasions; during this century it has not frozen properly at all. It's just as well the refrigerator and freezer were invented.

A symbolic last catch is shown being landed at Billingsgate Wharf on the Thames, before the 2000-year-old fish market moved to its new site on the Isle of Dogs in 1981. Porters wore their traditional 'leathers' – hats made from leather and hundreds of rivets – which were a prime necessity when they used to carry 30-stone (190-kg) trays of fish on their heads. Nowadays, the fish is moved around by trolley. When the fish industry first started to use ice, in the 1830s, farmers flooded their fields to help cope with the demand. Today, despite the invention of the refrigerator, the fish industry still uses vast quantities of ice to keep fish fresh.

THE MEN AND WOMEN FROM THE MET. Queen Victoria's daily diary was of the routine 'got up... had breakfast' variety, but one thing she never forgot to mention was the weather.

Her beloved Prince Albert set up meteorological stations at Osborne on the Isle of Wight and Braemar in Scotland and to this day, the Met. Office takes observations from a rain gauge strapped to the side of a Buckingham Palace greenhouse. It is badly sited, but no one has ever had the courage to complain.

Amateur weather enthusiasts have been part of the Met. Office team since its earliest days, and it still relies heavily on a network of volunteer observers. This network was largely the creation of one man, George Symons.

George Symons (1838–1900) was obsessed with rain. It is not an unusual obsession for a Briton, but instead of just talking about it, he measured it – in every possible container, in every possible place.

In order to get the kind of statistics he needed, he had to have help. In 1860, he had sympathisers keeping rainfall records at 168 stations all over Britain. In 1871, that figure had risen to 1504; by 1881 there were 2145, and by the time he died there were 3404 helpers. Today, there are about 5000 rain gauges in back gardens and fields, on lighthouses and at airports all over the country.

Symons's chief assistant in the early days was his mother. Later, his long-suffering wife, Elizabeth, helped him to deal with the mountains of correspondence and avalanches of figures that arrived at their house in Camden Square, London.

Besides keeping complicated rainfall tables, Symons devised an elaborate series of experiments to find out the best way of collecting the rain. For this he was able to tap the vast reservoir of talent represented throughout Britain by under-employed country vicars and retired colonels.

He also tried out the various kinds of thermometer screen available at the time and, on his advice, the Royal Meteorological Society adopted the familiar white wooden box, known as the Stevenson screen, around 1880. When the British Antarctic Expedition set off in 1910, three portable Stevenson screens, lent by the Met. Office, went with them. Even today they are still an essential part of every weather observer's equipment.

Ice and snow cover this Stevenson screen high up on Great Dun Fell in the Lake District. Early screens to shelter thermometers from the weather came in all shapes and sizes. One of the first, designed by a Dr George Martin of the Isle of Wight about 1838, was an open-sided thatched house complete with chimney. By the end of the century, however, the Stevenson screen dominated the field. It was named after Thomas Stevenson (father of Robert Louis Stevenson), who invented the double-louvre mechanism.

Satellite observations or, in earlier times, balloon and kite meteographs, can paint a broad impressionistic picture of weather movement. But for nitty-gritty climatological observation, there is no substitute for the person on the spot.

The Met. Office has a network of observers from Muckle Flugga in the Shetlands to St Mary's in the Isles of Scilly. All are enthusiasts, and many are unpaid. To qualify, they have to be prepared to meet the Met. Office's exacting standards and to commit themselves for at least 10 years.

'They're interested in the weather, that's all it is,' said Michael Weston, who oversees the network. 'The English are interested in the weather, aren't they? Some people are "volunteered" by their employers as part of the job. But after a while it settles down to one person who likes doing it, and that gets the best results. Finding someone in remote areas is sometimes difficult. What we ask is a 365-days-a year commitment.'

There are 320 climate stations in England and Wales, 130 in Scotland and 60 in Northern Ireland. Each site will have been visited and approved before being accepted into the network, and there are annual inspections. The Met. Office provides a Stevenson screen and rain gauge, with rigid guidelines about where to put them both. (A Stevenson screen must not be too near a patch of tarmac, for instance, because that would reflect heat and so distort the readings.) Observers have to keep their screens scrupulously clean, so they reflect an equal amount of sun. In industrial areas, that can mean washing them every week.

Rain gauges have to be emptied and thermometers checked on the dot of 9 a.m. GMT every morning. The Stevenson screen contains a wet bulb thermometer to show humidity, as well as a maximum and minimum thermometer.

Observers have to keep a weather diary for general observations about such things as cloud level – an area where they have the edge over automatic weather stations. There are machines that measure visibility, but they are still vastly expensive; the human eye has the distinct advantage of being free. Reports are made with a sequence of numbers; 00 means no cloud, 99 means a thunderstorm with hail.

Mrs Fran Lockyer runs a bed and breakfast business in an old lighthouse at Portland Bill in Dorset. She also finds time to take observations for the Met. Office five times a day, seven days a week. 'Luckily, I'm a fairly home-loving person: I don't go out a lot,' she said.

The morning observation, being the fullest, takes up to 20 minutes. Even if she has not finished clearing up after her bed and breakfast customers, Mrs Lockyer will not miss her appointment in the garden. 'I'm afraid the Met. does come first with me,' she said.

The Rev. Tom Downs, a retired clergyman, sends observations from his home in Penrith once a day. 'It's something I've always been interested in – particularly the clouds, watching the movement of the birds and so on,' said the Rev. Downs. 'Clouds are something I think most people take for granted and don't really look at. Local people do ask me what I think the weather's going to be, but I think the BBC and their weather reports are more accurate than mine.'

Measurement is, by definition, an exact science. But it is also a science which still has room for the enthusiastic amateur. This book began with the story of the pound, a story dominated by the figure of the Rev. Sheepshanks, hunched over his iron bars in the cellars of Somerset House. So it is fitting that it should end as it began, with amateurs – the retired clergyman, and the landlady from Portland Bill.

At the turn of the century, measurements of temperature in the upper atmosphere were taken by attaching recording devices to kites and balloons. The balloon meteograph, (left), invented by W H Dines, was used from 1907 until 1940. The rubber balloon would burst at high altitude, when it would act as a parachute for the recording device. A sign attached to the canister offered a reward of five shillings to anyone who returned it to Kew Observatory. Kites using steel piano wire for greater strength were often strung together – sometimes with catastrophic results. The French meteorologist Teisserenc de Bort once had 11 kites on 4 miles (7 km) of wire trailing over Paris. The wire broke and became tangled up in a ship's propeller. It also jammed the connecting rods on the railway, cutting off all communication with Brittany on a day when all France was anxiously awaiting the result of the Dreyfus case.

FURTHER READING

LENGTH and WEIGHT

Seton Bennett, *The Yard and the Pound: A Short History* (Bulletin OIML, No. 115, June 1989)

R D Connor *The Weights and Measures of England* (H.M.S.O., London, 1981)

William Hallock, *The Evolution of Weights and Measures* (Macmillan, New York, 1906)

John Perry, *The Story of Standards* (Funk and Wagnalls, New York, 1955)

Howard Wall, *The Story of the Evolution of British Measures* (Talbot and Co., London, 1919)

Ronald E Zupko, *Revolution in Measurement* (American Philosophical Society, Philadelphia, 1990)

TIME

Anthony F Aveni, *Empires of Time* (Basic Books, New York, 1989)

John Darwin, *The Triumphs of Big Ben* (Robert Hale, London, 1986)

William Doyle, *The Oxford History of the French Revolution* (OUP, Oxford, 1990)

David S Landes, *Revolution in Time: Clocks and the Making of the Modern World* (Bel Knap Press, Cambridge, Mass., 1983)

Kenneth John Rose, *The Body in Time* (Wiley Science Editions, New York, 1988)

G J Whitrow, *Time in History* (OUP, Oxford, 1988)

John Noble Wilford, *The Mapmakers* (Junction, London, 1981)

TEMPERATURE

Sylvia P Beamon and Susan Roaf, *The Ice Houses of Britain* (Routledge, London, 1989)

W E Knowles Middleton, *A History of the Thermometer* (Johns Hopkins Press, Baltimore, 1966)

Negrelti and Zaimbra Ltd, *A Story of Temperature Measurement* (London, 1958)

INDEX